ON HIGHEST MISSION SENT

The Story of Health Care in Lamont, Alberta

ON HIGHEST MISSION SENT

The Story of Health Care in Lamont, Alberta

Trudy A. Harrold

LHCC
1999

Design: Diane Jensen
Editorial: Margaret L. Iveson, Mary E. Dawe
Photo consultant: Kirk Harrold
Project coordination: Aspengrove Communications,
Box 270, Lamont, Alberta TOB 2RO

ISBN 0-9686594-0-3

PRINTED AND BOUND IN CANADA

CONTENTS

ACKNOWLEDGEMENTS

A book such as this is only possible with the combined efforts of many people. I want to express my thanks:

To the Board of Lamont Health Care Centre for their vision of a book capturing the highlights of the hospital's history.

To the creative team who worked on this project: Diane Jensen, for her fine design layout and patience with my learning, Margaret L. Iveson and Mary E. Dawe for their gentle editorial expertise and guidance, and Kirk Harrold for substantial photographic support.

To those in the Administration Office of the Lamont Health Care Centre, who very kindly took the time to help locate necessary documents, files and information: Harold James, Dolores Sadoway, Anita Anderson, and Lorraine Field.

To the many people who responded willingly with photographs and stories when I needed them: Bernice Schneider, Kent and Shirley Harrold, Doris Andrais, Mae Adamyk, June Johnston, Pearl Letwin, Ellis Oberle, Shirley Olynyk and Sheila Vilcsak.

To my family and friends, who have supported me in so many ways while I completed this project.

PREFACE

The word "mission" means "the special duty for which one is sent, or a special task to which one devotes one's life". When the decision in 1916 was made to use Summo Commisso Missi – "On Highest Mission Sent"– as the motto of the School of Nursing at Lamont, the concept of mission was embedded in religion and drew its strength from a social structure that supported such endeavors. Although changes have occured over time, the concept of mission still has value. Today, "mission statements" give a sense of direction and purpose to many organizations and institutions.

The sense of mission has been integral to the provision of health care at Lamont, from its modest beginnings as a cottage-type hospital with a small staff, through its years with the Nursing School, to the integrated health care complex opened in 1999. Over the years, many people have treated their work here as "a special duty for which one is sent", and many people have devoted their lives to it.

This book is dedicated to all those who have made the hospital at Lamont a special place – throughout the past, in the present, and for the future.

KIRK HARROLD

"Wildflowers in great profusion and of almost endless variety made their appearance to greet the newcomer."

– Clement Hoyler, local pastor, 1896

CHAPTER 1

PRE 1900 TO 1911

DEDICATED BEGINNINGS

The story of the development of health care in Lamont, Alberta begins in the years before the hospital was built, before Lamont was a town, before Alberta was a province. It begins in a parkland landscape used extensively by native people for hunting buffalo, beaver and muskrat. Fur had been the gold that brought early non-native people to the West, but by the late 1880's and early 1890's a new settlement movement was beginning. Early in 1887, prospective settlers William Cammack and William Robertson ventured from Nebraska to the Lamont area, to take a look at the land as a possible homestead location. In 1892, they chose to return to homestead in the area.

FROM BUSH TO BUSHELS

Bush home of Moravian settlers family, 1894

Records suggest that 1892 was the beginning of what became a great wave of immigration to the area. Among the first to arrive were settlers from the Parry Sound area of Ontario. Many of them came to homestead, but among them were a few professional men and shopkeepers. Approximately two townships in the area were settled by people from Eastern Canada and the United States.

Families from Europe also began to make their way to the area from 1891 onward. An immigration policy, initiated by Clifford Sifton, encouraged colonization of the West. With the promise of land to homestead, people came from oppressed areas in Central and Eastern Europe, including Galicia, Bukovina, Bessarabia and Romania to begin a new life for their families.

Most of the settlers here were of Ukrainian origin from Eastern Europe. At the time of their arrival they were called "Ruski," "Russenne," "Galicians," and "Ruthenians," as the word Ukrainian was forbidden in the old country and was not put down on the passage documents.

– Michael Kozak
Alice (Kozak) Krywoniuk

ALONG VICTORIA TRAIL

ALONG VICTORIA TRAIL

Mrs. Nemirsky, Sr. and
Mrs. Theo Nemirsky in front of
their first sod roof home, 1899

Wasyl Eleniak is recognized as the first Ukrainian settler in the area, followed by many others who came with hopes for the future. They settled in the area north and east of the present site of Lamont, eventually numbering 40 – 60 000 in the largest settlement of its kind in western Canada. To the west, there was a fairly compact settlement of German-speaking people from southern Russia, many of them of Moravian and Lutheran faiths.

Life was hard for many of these early homesteaders. Often living at a subsistence level, they suffered from a lack of money and resources, frequent illness, accidents, and vagrant weather in an unfamiliar land that was a long way from their original home. It was their hard work, determination and sometimes good fortune that allowed those who stayed and survived to build a new life. Building a home was the first priority for most, as they needed shelter where there was none. They raised their own food, and slowly acquired livestock and tools to help them build their holdings.

Medical care in those early years was minimal. Michael Kozak and Alice (Kozak) Krywoniuk commented in a local history book that "Medical services were no nearer than the City of Edmonton, so they had to depend on home remedies. It was a case of the fittest survived, and some didn't."

In the same book, there are references to two women who assisted families with home remedies and care during these difficult times. A woman known as Grandmother Milsap (Catherine Milsap) was a nurse and looked after many of the sick folks day or night. She was, according to her granddaughter Irene (Hackett) Stainton, "a real blessing to many a poor, lonely, sick person. Some who were really sick with loneliness, were greatly cheered and encouraged by her sympathy, her pleasant personality and kindly spirit. The courage and concern for others that was part of her being was truly amazing, as she walked those many miles between the homes."

Sophie Porayko Kyforuk, an early resident, tells of another woman, Magdalena Nemirsky, who was a "remarkable, self-taught pioneer, oldest among us... [who was] knowledgeable in folk medicine. She set broken bones, managed hernias, sprains, delivered babies, and knew about herbal remedies." Magdalena had arrived in Canada with her sons Constantine and Theodore in April, 1896, settling in the area later known as Wostok. Theodore would later go on to play a role in the hospital at Lamont, acting as an important link to the large Ukrainian settlement.

Schools were established early in the settlement years, often filled with children who could not speak English. One of these schools, Beaver Creek, was established in 1896 and a hamlet called Edna grew up a mile east of the school. In 1901, Dr. Harry R. Smith began a medical practice in Edna (later renamed Star and moved to its present location). Dr. Smith was a member of the Student Volunteer Union doing missionary work in Canada. He was joined in his work in 1902 by his wife, Dr. Martha Doyle, also a worker in the Student Volunteer Union. Dr. Smith and Dr. Doyle were attracted to this area because the need for medical services was crucial. They came here under the direction of the Home Mission Board of the Methodist Church, although they practiced privately, without the support of the Methodist Church.

As the waves of immigration swept over Canada, Churches as a whole saw the opportunity for expansion, influence and continued service to God. Roman Catholic, Anglican, Methodist and Presbyterian Churches were actively preaching, teaching and healing in mission centres throughout the region. The first attempt of the Methodist Church in the field of medical missions among the European settlers in Alberta was in 1901, when Dr. C.H. Lawford was stationed at the settlement at Victoria (along the North Saskatchewan River, 35 miles north of the Lamont area). Later in 1906, with the support of the Mission Board of the Methodist Church, a hospital was built at nearby Pakan, on the north side of the North Saskatchewan River. The Methodist Church recognized the special needs of the district, offering financial support and taking on responsibilities that facilitated the development of medical services, not only in Pakan but in other communities, which ultimately included Lamont.

VICTORIA SETTLEMENT BROCHURE, Alberta Culture

Dr. C.H. Lawford served as Victoria-Pakan's Methodist minister and medical doctor, 1901-22

VICTORIA SETTLEMENT BROCHURE, Alberta Culture

The Methodist George McDougall Hospital opened to Victoria-Pakan patients in 1907

Albert Ernest Archer was born in Campbellford, Ontario, December 14, 1878. His parents were Reverend Joseph Archer and Martha Hardy. He took his public school training mostly in Port Rowan, although the family moved quite often because Methodist ministers were regularly posted to new locations. A strong interest in botany, nature study and microscopes absorbed him throughout his early years. His high school training was completed at Hamilton Collegiate and St. Catharine's High School. Following his graduation, he took a Teacher Training Course at the Welland Model School. He taught for a very short period of time before entering medical studies at the University of Toronto.

Early in 1903, however, Dr. Doyle died unexpectedly soon after the birth of their first child. In July, 1903, Dr. Smith moved to Edmonton, to a house on First Street. (He would later be professionally associated with the Royal Alexandra Hospital from 1921-1928.) His presence in the Star-Edna area, however, was not forgotten. For people like Sophie Porayko Kyforuk, he was a life-saver: "In 1901 he brought me back to life after buffalo bean poisoning and later attended to my brother's gunshot wound received from an accidentally discharged gun."

Dr. Smith apparently knew Dr. Albert E. Archer from their studies together at the University of Toronto. Dr. Archer's father, Reverend Joseph Archer, was a Methodist minister who possessed a "missionary zeal and spirit" which had apparently found its way into Albert E. Archer's genes. Dr. Archer had wanted to go to China as a medical missionary after he had completed his training at the University of Toronto in 1903, but the Boxer Rebellion prevented that dream from being realized. When Dr. Smith wrote to Albert telling him of the large Ukrainian settlement northeast of Edmonton which was in need of medical services, Albert decided instead to go west to Star, North West Territories. In the summer of 1903, Dr. Archer moved to Star and took over Dr. Smith's practice.

LPH/AMH ALUMNAE COLLECTION

Dr. A.E. Archer (back, right) with his parents and siblings

Hamilton City Hospital was the location of Dr. Archer's internship, where he met his wife-to-be, Jessie Walker Valens, of Lucknow, Ontario. As her parents would not allow her to be married until she graduated in 1904, Jessie joined Albert after his arrival at Star. Their daughter, Margaret (Archer) Buchanan, later relates, "Within days of her arrival, mother was accompanying dad by horse and buggy, over prairie trails to help him with house calls. Gradually the recent immigrants from Europe were growing to trust the doctor, and I am sure it was reassuring to them to have his wife come along to do what she could to help."

ALONG VICTORIA TRAIL

Jessie Valens before her marriage to Dr. Archer

Jessie Archer also was instrumental in assisting with much of the kitchen table surgery that was so often a necessity under the less than perfect conditions. Jessie had been trained to administer anaesthetics. In fact, there was a law in the statute books of Alberta that stated that "no anaesthetic might be administered by other than a medical practitioner and Mrs. A.E. Archer of Lamont."

Dr. Archer's early practice with the settlers and homesteaders in the area became a story of courage, faithfulness and dedication that echoes the work of many of the early pioneering doctors in the west. It was often difficult for a doctor to reach the people who needed help. Sometimes too, people had no money to pay for the doctor's care. There were no sterilized environments or special equipment for the doctor to use in his practice.

To complicate matters, the immigrants from Europe often possessed a fatalistic attitude about health matters. There were two common sayings of the people: "Shcho buda, te buda" ("What will be, will be") and "Bozsha Volyah" ("God wills it") that made care a constant challenge. The people had experienced little contact with medical professionals in their homeland because physicians and surgeons had served only the wealthy. Dr. Archer improvised to find ways to reach the people. Florence Love relates that "By wearing a bowler hat and a top-coat with a cape, so the story goes, Dr. Archer hoped to add age and dignity to his very youthful appearance. The people from the old country thought he was some dignitary from their church and in their faith bowed before him. They soon learned that his work was no less dedicated and that he was permanently there to minister to them."

Soon after Dr. Archer's arrival at Star, he attended to a maternity case in which the mother had developed a postpartum infection. Dr. Archer went to the home, but was unable to save the woman and she died the next day. Three days later, Dr. Archer was called to attend another woman in labour, only to discover that it was in the same home and the same bed as the previous patient who had died. When he made a follow-up call three days later (after a heavy rain which made travel difficult) he was surprised to be greeted by the young woman with her new baby on her back, walking through a deep puddle, as he arrived with his team and buggy.

ALONG VICTORIA TRAIL

C.N.R. laying tracks near Lamont, 1905

By 1905, the Canadian Northern Railway had surveyed a line south of the settlement at Star, near the location of Bloomfield School (later known as Lamont Elementary School) established in 1902. A townsite was also surveyed, with Main Street running from the station to a footbridge on King Street, and Railway Avenue running parallel to the railway tracks.

Once the railway had been completed, Dr. and Mrs. Archer decided to move their family of two children (Norman and Margaret at that time), and their house, to Lamont. During the winter of 1906-1907, there were several buildings moved on skids from Star, to be closer to the railway and services that were developing in the Lamont town site. The community was growing and Dr. Archer and Robert Torrie bought a tract of land from Joseph Alton, had it subdivided and sold as building lots.

As a child, I envied my brother Norman, who rode with mother, across the prairie, in the house, as it was moved from its foundation and rolled on logs, pulled by twelve teams of horses, to Lamont. I remember my father telling me that the only real difficulty was in crossing the Beaver Creek!

– Margaret (Archer) Buchanan

ALONG VICTORIA TRAIL

Moving Dr. Archer's house to Lamont, 1906

The Archers were, from the beginning, involved in the Methodist Church community. During 1906, Dr. Archer served on the building committee for the church to be built by the Methodists and Presbyterians. The Lamont Church was completed in 1906, serving both denominations. Services alternated Sunday morning and evening, a common practice in the days before the Methodist and Presbyterian churches united. A manse for the Presbyterian minister and a parsonage for the Methodist minister were built in 1907.

ALONG VICTORIA TRAIL

Dr. Archer participated in the Building Committee for the church built by the Presbyterians and Methodists, 1906

Front row: Joe Alton, M. Munroe, R. Swan

Back row: Dr. A.E. Archer, R.J. Torrie, Ira Wright

ALONG VICTORIA TRAIL

The Lamont Church, 1906

The Union Church was opened with adequate dignity and ceremony on November 19, 1906. The last item of activity was a fine church supper. The Doctor was halfway through his meal when he was handed a telegram which stated that a man at Brosseau wanted a doctor and that it was probably urgent. Brosseau was on the Saskatchewan River some sixty miles north east of Lamont. Duty first and duty last persuaded Dr. Archer to set out at 7 p.m. for Brosseau. He would drive his own horses to Andrew, a distance of 25 miles, and there he would put them in a livery barn and take another team for the remainder of the trip. He arrived at Brosseau around 6 a.m. and coming to the home he had been directed to he saw a faint light bobbing here and there about the farmyard. The lantern was carried by a man in his thirties. The ensuing conversation was much as follows –

"Good morning." "Good morning." "Did someone from here send for a doctor?" "Yes." "Who is it that wants to see him?" "I do." "You do not look very sick." "I'm not." "Well why then did you send for a doctor?" "Because I read in the Montreal Star that everyone should be examined by a doctor at least once a year, and I thought that I had better have it done." Dr. Archer advised the patient to call at his office the next time he was in Lamont then turned around and headed back to Andrew where he again changed teams and continued on his way home. The patient was unable to pay for the trip 'just then' or ever, so far as I know. Furthermore Archer paid the livery man in Andrew for the use of his team.

– Morley A.R. Young

View of Lamont, around 1907

ALONG VICTORIA TRAIL

R.E. Harrison and his drug store

ALONG VICTORIA TRAIL

By 1907, Lamont was becoming a thriving community. With the opening of R.E. Harrison's drug store, J.K. Pendelton's Real Estate office, Ludwig Lilge's store, Thomas Dallas' Hardware store, a lumber yard and livery stable, the town was beginning to take on the character of a bustling centre. Several other businesses from Star were moved to Lamont at the same time that Dr. Archer moved, among them Walker and Reid and Co., General Merchants.

A new two-room brick school was built in 1908, under the name of Bloomfield School District 641 of the Province of Alberta, to serve the growing number of families in the area.

Two room brick school building

ALONG VICTORIA TRAIL

The Archers continued to minister to the medical needs of the people, while establishing their own home and family. They built a new, larger house in 1910, using the same type of cinder blocks that had been used earlier in the construction of the parsonage and manse. Sometimes their home became more than a home. We learn from Eleanor Challenger that about 1907, "there was an outbreak of typhoid fever and Dr. Archer put up a big tent in his back yard to use as a hospital." It was becoming increasingly apparent that there needed to be a place where patients could come for medical help.

ALONG VICTORIA TRAIL

Dr. and Mrs. Archer with Norman and Margaret, 1909

In 1911, a committee was formed to explore the option of building a hospital in Lamont. The record reads: "At the Annual Conference of the Alberta Methodists, held in Calgary in May, 1911, a scheme for the building or purchasing a hospital in Lamont was approved. The Conference appointed the following committee to meet in Lamont on Tuesday, June 6, 1911, to decide on the scheme and devise ways and means of finance. The following men were named to the committee: Dr. A.E. Archer (Lamont), Dr. H.R. Smith (Edmonton), F.C. Smith (Lamont), Rev. T.C. Buchanan (Calgary – Superintendent of Home Missions of the Methodist Church), W.G. McGrath (Edmonton), W.H. White, M.P. (Fort Saskatchewan), F.A. Walker, M.P.P. (Fort Saskatchewan), Rev. W.G. Shaw (Lamont), Robert Swan (Lamont), James Hackett (Lamont), Rev. J.K. Smith (Chipman), A.T. Cushing (Edmonton), Dr. Riddell (Edmonton), Dr. C.H. Lawford (Pakan), R.E. Harrison (Lamont)."

Two meetings of this committee were held, under the chairmanship of Dr. Archer, at which R.E. Harrison was secretary and Rev. W.C. Shaw was treasurer. The July 12, 1911 minutes indicate that "This committee is in favor

Dr. Archer was also involved in other needs of those in the community. Soon after the newly established Elk Island Park was opened in June, 1907, John Kmech "had trapped two moose with the idea of training them to use for farm work. He was not making much headway. Somehow Dr. Archer heard about the moose and kindly offered to buy them. He paid one hundred dollars for the two moose and released them in Elk Island Park, which had just been established. The money was used to buy a horse, and Dr. Archer's generosity was long remembered. No doubt the descendants of John's moose are still roaming through the Park."

– Annie Melnyk

of building a hospital in Lamont, providing the Village Corporation vote $1000.00 toward building of same and will build a sidewalk and grade road to same." By July 25, 1911, the Hospital Committee had become the Hospital Board.

LPH/AMH ALUMNAE COLLECTION

Dr. A.E. Archer

The financing of the facility was based on the procurement of local subscriptions, with support of the Board of Home Missions of the Methodist Church. Architect G.H. MacDonald was asked "to draw up plans and specifications and call for tenders for the building of a brick, brick veneer or frame building, to cost not more than $7000.00 including heating, plumbing, and stationary equipment, same to accommodate about 16 beds".

The land for the hospital was purchased from Joe Alton, and Joe Knight was employed as building superintendent at a wage of six dollars per day. As the building progressed, it was determined that finances would allow the finishing of the attic to permit two more rooms in the hospital.

Arrangements were made to open the hospital on Labour Day, September 12, 1912. At the board meeting on August 3, 1912, Dr. Archer was appointed Medical Superintendent of the new hospital. At a subsequent meeting held August 20, 1912, there was a mention made of Dr. William T. Rush, who came to join Dr. Archer. (Dr. Rush apparently became a board member immediately, since he is recorded as having made a motion during that meeting.) Dr. Rush's background included medical work in Vegreville and Leduc, as well as mission work with first-nations peoples in British Columbia. He would become an asset to the hospital: in addition to his medical work, he assumed responsibility for the business affairs of the hospital.

LPH/AMH ALUMNAE COLLECTION

Dr. W.T. Rush

With the building of the new hospital, the dedication and care shown by those early people who settled here in Lamont would now take a new form. The courage of the early pioneers, the commitment of the Archers, the support of the townspeople, the immigrants' growing faith in medical care and the involvement of the Church in providing healing and ministry to those in the new land all came together, to usher in the next era of medical care at Lamont.

ALONG VICTORIA TRAIL

Lamont Public Hospital completed, with Dr. A.E. Archer and Dr. W.T. Rush, 1912

CHAPTER 2
1912 TO 1920
BUILDING A VISION

On September 2, 1912, official opening day of the new hospital at Lamont, invited dignitaries, community supporters and curious onlookers turned out to celebrate. Florence Love recounts that "it was a day of happiness and joy for the people of the town of Lamont and Community. The Ladies' Aid of the Church went all out to provide food for the crowds in attendance. There were sports for old and young. The Lamont Brass Band gave its best."

AHA HOSPITAL

Opening Ceremonies, Lamont Public Hospital, September 2, 1912

A four storey frame building; in the basement the kitchen, dining room, three bedrooms, (for domestic help) the laundry and furnace rooms. On the first floor was the office, chart room, nurses' sitting room, dispensary, two private rooms, one semi-private, the men's ward and bathroom. On the second floor were the operating and sterilizing rooms, maternity ward and the same number of other wards, bath, etc. as on the first floor. There was also a bed or sometimes two or three cots on the small balcony off the second floor.

As the hospital grew and the staff was increased, three rooms were rented for the students in the Harvey Harris boarding house. There was a room for the night nurse at the parsonage or manse. Later the Torrie home was acquired and used by the nurses until the nurses' home was built.

– Bessie (Tillapaugh) Long, entered training in 1913

The Honorable Duncan Marshall, Minister of Agriculture and Health for the Province of Alberta was present, as was Dr. J.H. Riddel, Principal of Alberta College in Edmonton, Frank Walker, M.P.P. for the Victoria Constituency, Rev. T.C. Buchanan, Superintendent of Missions for the Methodist Church in Alberta, and Theodore Nemirsky, representing the Greek Orthodox part of the community.

In an article that appeared in 1916, four years after the hospital opened, Miriam Elston wrote about that opening-day ceremonies. She thought that some of the people who came to that opening went away from it with their vision enlarged as to the importance of the event. The men who had come to speak at the opening were men of vision – doctors, university professors and members of parliament, who underscored the importance of meeting the needs of this community.

THE LAMP IS GOLDEN

The Lamont Brass Band on the steps of the new hospital, September 2, 1912

ALONG VICTORIA TRAIL

Theodore Nemirsky speaking to crowds on opening day

Among those speakers was Theodore Nemirsky, whom Elston says was "of advanced thought himself, and deeply interested in the modern methods of treatment of diseases." He spoke in his native Ruthenian tongue to those gathered who were dressed in the distinctive garb of the Russian and Ukrainian peasant. Because of the poverty of some of these people and their fatalistic attitudes, Nemirsky knew that the hospital held hope for the people, and he encouraged their acceptance of this new place for medical care.

The cottage-type frame building was built to accommodate 15 beds in a 37 by 43 foot building. Final costs were estimated at between $15,000 and $15,500, of which the community raised $12,500 to $13,000, and the Board of Home Missions of the Methodist Church contributed $2500.

The Lamont Public Hospital opened with its first staff in place. Medical staff included, of course, Dr. A.E. Archer, the Superintendent of the Hospital, and Dr. W.T. Rush. The first Matron of the hospital, on duty on opening day, was Miss Vellettia Shuttleworth. She had previously been with the Methodist Mission Board.

Miss Bella McGillivary was the first of the domestic staff at the new hospital. She did the cooking, housekeeping and general maid duties. She was later succeeded by Miss Scott who was the first official housekeeper. Maintenance tasks were done by the occasional handyman or by a patient who might stay a few days or weeks after a hospital convalescence. Young students attending the school in town also helped in their off hours from school.

LPH/AMH ALUMNAE COLLECTION

Miss Shuttleworth, first Matron, 1912-1913

That same day, shortly after the opening ceremonies were concluded, young Charles Whittaker, employed by the village, arrived at the hospital. Because he had a serious case of typhoid fever, he became the first patient to be admitted to the hospital. Since only Miss Shuttleworth was on duty, Mrs. F.C. Smith came from the community to help with the nursing. The next day, Miss Effie Johnston (who was in the district preparing for her marriage) came to assist with the nursing, and stayed on for three weeks.

Charlie Whittaker, first patient, with nurses Miss Reid (left) and Miss Purschke (right)

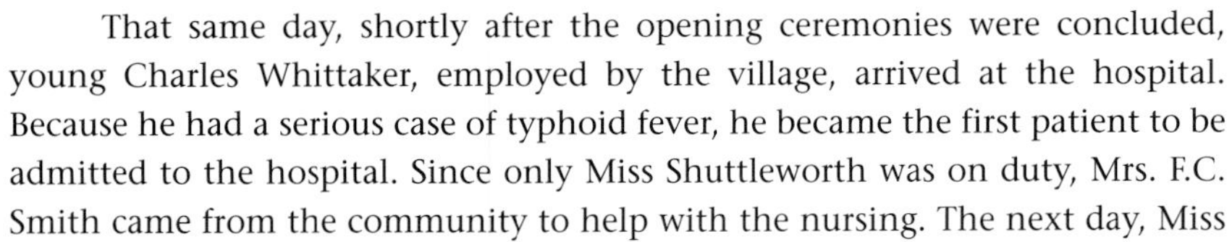

LPH/AMH ALUMNAE COLLECTION

From its inception, the Lamont Hospital offered training to new nurses, a tradition which would be carried on for the next 60 years. Dr. Archer, in conversation with his daughter later, explained why he thought a nursing school was so important: "Well-trained nurses... who had been taught not only nursing skills, but the compassionate, personal treatment of their patients, would practice in other areas and other hospitals, and so their influence would be far-spread..."

THE LAMP IS GOLDEN

Annie Purschke, first nurse to graduate from Lamont Public Hospital

The first probationer, Martha Garvin, must have arrived at Lamont a few days after the hospital opened. Unfortunately, she was only with the hospital until June, 1913. A second student, Fannie Stafford, arrived on September 26, 1912, but was unable to complete her program until 1918 because of illness. Annie Purschke, a local girl, became the first student to complete a training program at the new Lamont Public Hospital, becoming its first graduate nurse in 1915. Annie came from a pioneer family who had been in the area since 1894. Her mother, Mary Purschke, was a practical nurse who offered her nursing and midwife skills to the community for many years, both before and after the arrival of doctors in the area.

As with any institution, there were other firsts. On October 8, 1912, Amy Eaton was admitted to the hospital. She had been visiting her family at Mundare, where her father was the principal at the school. She became ill and required surgery, which was performed by Dr. Archer and Dr. Reid of Vegreville (Dr. Rush was away at the time). The surgery was serious enough to require a blood transfusion, so Dr. Archer arranged for Amy's brother, Donald, to be the donor. It was the first transfusion recorded at this hospital and is thought to have been the first one recorded in Alberta.

The first baby to be born at Lamont Public Hospital arrived on October 14, 1912. Mr and Mrs. William Hackett had a daughter, who was subsequently named Vellettia after Miss Shuttleworth, the Matron.

Another first for the Archers was in 1912, with the arrival of a Ford car, which made travel around the district somewhat easier, but only in good weather. Dr. Archer apparently became a good mechanic, because there was no garage closer than Edmonton. When something would go wrong, he would take the car apart, lay out all the pieces on newspapers on the lawn, and follow the instruction book to clean and reassemble the parts, hoping he did not have any parts left over.

The community was always an active participant in hospital matters, making sure there were sufficient supplies of meat, butter, eggs and milk. The Lamont Public Hospital Aid Society was formed in 1912 by women of the community, to assist with many matters of a practical nature. They sewed such necessities as sheets and hospital gowns, raised funds through bake sales and teas, and ensured supplies of vegetables and preserves to last through the long winter months.

The Methodist Church continued its support of the hospital, with the arrival of Rev. J.K. Smith in 1912, as a missionary of the Methodist Church. He was able to speak Ukrainian, a great help in patient care, because he could act as an interpreter whenever needed. Reverend Smith was succeeded by the Reverend C.W.W. Ross who had arrived in 1914. Because Reverend Ross was also fluent in the language of many of the patients, he was able to relieve their anxieties about hospitalization. He also helped the nurses with matters more practical, often staying to help with a stubborn pump that would not work, or restocking the furnace fire.

THE LAMP IS GOLDEN

Miss Slaughter, Matron, 1913-1917

In 1913, Miss Sarah Slaughter, a graduate of the Massachusetts General Hospital of Boston, replaced Miss Shuttleworth. Miss Slaughter had come to the hospital early in 1913 to nurse on staff, then took over when Miss Shuttleworth went on to work at the Nurses' Registry in Edmonton. Miss Slaughter was respected and loved by all, as the following quote from a student nurse suggests: "Miss Slaughter... gave us our training on a very high standard... working under the handicaps of those growing years, she never faltered, we could always depend on her to stand by us at all times... she was one of those women one wanted to work for... always true to her students, yet very firm." Unfortunately, Miss Slaughter passed away in the Lamont Hospital in 1917. It was felt by some that she deserved a medal for her work in the Lamont Public Hospital.

The first year of operation of the hospital was not without difficult moments. The doctors still travelled out to the countryside, often returning with a patient. Nurses took care of the admitting, as well as patient comfort, treatment according to doctor's orders, keeping the physical plant operating (furnace, water, and light), and often cooking a patient's meal or washing a newborn's laundry as well. Shifts were long and off duty hours were scarce. The little tin lamps that illuminated the hallways during the night hours were under the night nurse's constant vigilance. Occasionally, during the failure of other auxiliary power sources, a nurse might be found standing on a chair holding a lamp during an operation so that the operation could continue.

While I didn't mind the nights in summer, I dreaded the winter months as there was always one or two trips each night to be made to the furnace room, to shake down and stoke up the furnace. Carrying a lamp thru the dark hall to the furnace room and back to the first floor wasn't a bit of fun for me!

– Bessie (Tillapaugh) Long

The early nurses often went along with the doctors out in to the country to help with maternity cases. A nurse of that time writes, "It was not unusual to go into a home to find mother, father and several children in one or two rooms and have to dig for the mother under a feather quilt. Until we packed the "Mat Bag" for the doctors, the quilt would be all we had to drape the mother with. Often we found only a tin pie plate or a granite cup to boil anything that needed boiling."

The "Mat Bag", short for Maternity Bag, was packed with all the supplies that were commonly used in a delivery. It facilitated the tasks of the nurses and doctors called out to deliveries in the home.

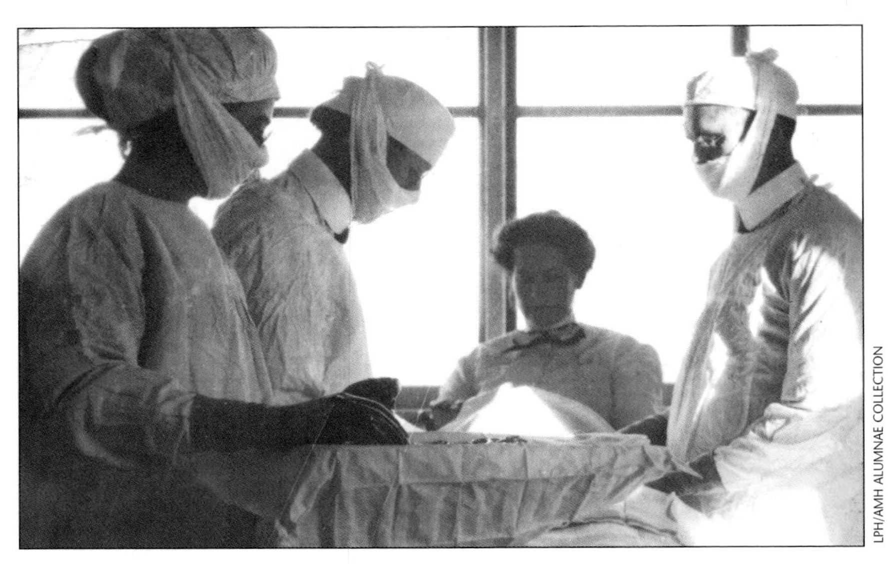

LPH/AMH ALUMNAE COLLECTION

In the operating room
Left to right: Miss Slaughter, Dr. Archer, Mrs. Archer, Dr. Rush

Lamont Public Hospital began to attract notice, as this quote from the *Christian Guardian* of October 8, 1913, would suggest:

"Already in the short span of one year, the institution has gained a most enviable reputation in a large constituency of its own, and has even attracted patients from large centers where hospital facilities are more elaborate. It is, in short, the case of a rural community enjoying a hospital service equal in efficiency to that available in cities. This is important, as the moral influence of such an institution depends on its effectiveness. To this is added the expression of Christian sympathy in a personal relationship."

The first graduation exercise for nurses at Lamont Public Hospital was held in 1915. The lone participant was Annie Purschke. A newspaper clipping from the time says that the event, "although short, was excellent. Altogether, Lamont always proud of its hospital, was never prouder than on Tuesday evening and the good wishes of the entire community are with its first graduate nurse."

Miriam Elston's 1916 article called "Meeting the Needs on the Frontier – My acquaintance with Lamont Public Hospital" shared stories about some of the early patients at the Hospital. She indicated that since the opening of the Hospital almost 1500 patients had been admitted for longer or shorter stays, and several hundred more had received treatment of varying kinds. A number of these patients were children. One of these, Lena, suffered from rickets and had never walked before she was admitted to the hospital at the age of two and a half years. Her stay in the hospital was eight months long. By the end of it, Elston reports, she was "a hale and hearty little specimen of humanity, and is very sure on her feet running wherever she pleases." Another child Nick, was a resident of the hospital for a year. These children were the first of many for whom the hospital became home.

LPH/AMH ALUMNAE COLLECTION

Lena with student nurse
Agnes Townsend, 1915

The second class of graduating nurses, in 1916, included Kay Reid, Bessie Tillapaugh and Agnes Townsend. The guest speaker at their graduation exercises was Dr. Edgar Allin, who practiced in Edmonton. The story is told that Edgar brought a bouquet of roses for each of the nurses, a gesture that was much appreciated by all and one that formed a tradition that was to be carried on for many years.

In 1917, Miss Christine Musselman, a graduate of Vancouver General Hospital became Matron. She remained in this position until her marriage in 1919 to R.E. Harrison. In addition to sometimes being the only graduate nurse on duty 24 hours at a time, Miss Musselman was an instructress for the nursing students. She joined Dr. Archer and Dr. Rush in formalizing and offering a course of lectures in late 1917 or early 1918. (Prior to 1917, lectures were given by Dr. Rush and were taken from the "Chataqua Course for Nurses". Lectures were offered sporadically, whenever doctors and nurses could find the time.) A quote from an alumnae history states that "To Miss Musselman goes the credit for establishing a course of lectures in line with those of the times."

LPH/AMH ALUMNAE COLLECTION

Miss Musselman, Matron, 1917-1919

LPH/AMH ALUMNAE COLLECTION

Miss Musselman and the nurses, 1918
In this photo, the nurses' uniforms of this time can be seen

Miss Musselman was also instrumental in creating other changes. The first uniform of the nurses underwent changes, to be more like those of Miss Musselman's training school. The dress was of blue cotton or denim type material with a fine white stripe. This was overlaid with a bib of white cotton, crossed in the back with an all-round apron of the same type of cotton. The collar was a stiffly starched cotton or linen with square ends, and the cuffs, also starched, were white cotton about eight inches long. The cap was of the same cotton, but with no distinguishing bands. The hem-line was eight inches from the floor. Black boots with rubber heels were worn with black cotton stockings.

Sometimes when we were in need of hot water, we depended on the cook's good nature to let us have some from the kitchen stove. One day, for an emergency, one of the nurses ran to the kitchen. No one was around – so the water in a kettle on the stove was poured into a pitcher and sent up on the lift. That night when we were all seated at the supper table, the cook inquired (a little too politely for comfort) just who had taken the kettle of syrup she had ready to use in canning fruit, and whatever was it used for? I do not believe she ever found out, nor did the patient who had the enema!

– Bessie (Tillapaugh) Long

Graduation pins: In 1915, Annie Purschke was presented with a gold pin at graduation which was a circle containing the letters L.P.H. The pin was approximately the size off a twenty-five cent piece in diameter and thickness. Gold lettering and an encircling gold rim were laid on white enamel. Later a gold bar was attached, medallion style, on which the year of graduation could be engraved. After 1950, the words "Archer Memorial Hospital" were engraved on the gold bar.

The local community again shouldered most of the responsibility of fund raising (for the 1917 additions) but felt that since folk were coming from many miles away to get hospital care that someone other than the local people should share the financial load. It was at this time that the Home Mission Board of the Methodist Church became more interested in the Lamont Public Hospital. The Rev. T.C. Buchanan, Superintendent of Home Missions of the Methodist Church in Alberta and Dr. Archer presented the needs of the hospital and the community to the Mission Board. The result was that the operation of the hospital became the responsibility of the Mission Board some three years after its opening. At Church Union in 1925 (the union of the Methodists and Presbyterians) this responsibility was passed on to the United Church of Canada under whose auspices the hospital still functions.

– Morley A.R. Young

Miss Musselman also introduced a silver bar pin which was worn at the collar of the uniform. It had a white shield with a red cross placed in the centre of the bar. The class year as well as the letters L.P.H. were engraved on the silver bar. Later, pin cuffs were added to the uniform as well; both the cuff pins and the collar pin were worn throughout training.

Changes were also made to the hospital building itself. By 1917, it had become evident that the hospital was over-extended and required an enlargement. When the new additions were completed, the hospital officially accommodated 30 beds, although the hospital could accommodate 45 patients, not including bassinettes. The cost of the project was $17,000, half of which was raised by the local community and the remainder paid for by the Methodist Church. The third floor received the benefit of most of the additions and renovations. Four wards, a diet kitchen, a service room and bathroom, and two staff bedrooms were added. Three verandas were also added to the east side of the building, one on each floor. These were largely used for patients receiving the accepted "fresh-air" treatment of the day.

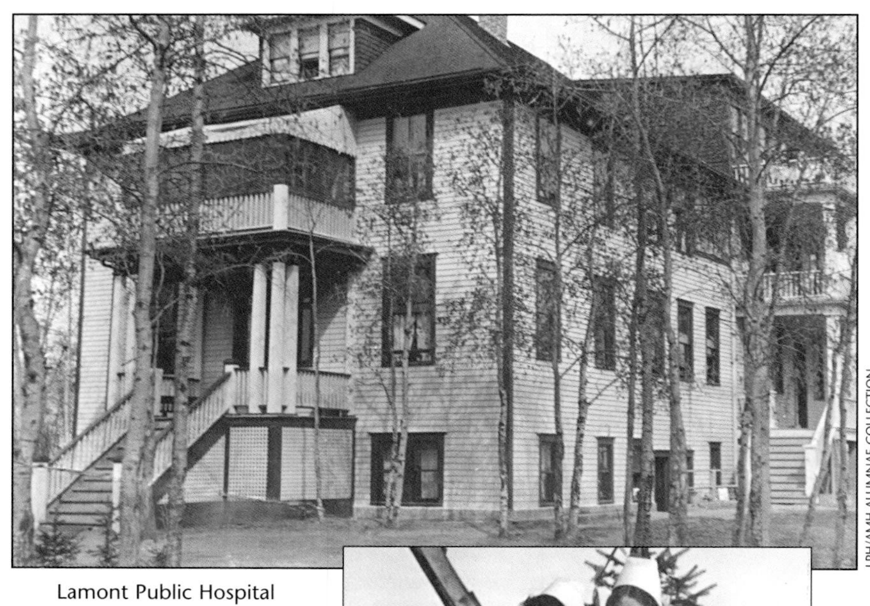

LPH/AMH ALUMNAE COLLECTION

Lamont Public Hospital after additions, 1917

Patients receiving the "fresh-air" treatment of the day, on the third floor veranda

LPH/AMH ALUMNAE COLLECTION

THE LAMP IS GOLDEN

Nurses' Home, 1917

The Women's Missionary Society was a strong component of the Methodist Church's Mission work. They operated a number of mission hospitals across western Canada (11 hospitals and four nursing units as of 1925) providing support in the form of grants, funding and staffing. At Lamont, the Women's Missionary Society's support took the form of funds for the building of the 1917 Home and later renovations, as well as contributing a grant toward the salary of the Superintendent of Nurses.

In this same year, 1917, the first Nurses' Home became a reality, through the support of the Women's Missionary Society of the Methodist Church. The building was a frame building, like the hospital, painted a cream color with brown trim. It was a simple square building, four steps leading to a front door, with a side door that faced the side door of the hospital for easy movement of nurses to and from the hospital. There were eight rooms: six rooms for the student nurses, each accommodating two or three nurses, one room for the matron and one sitting room for general use. There was a bathroom on each floor. Steam heating piped from the hospital kept things warm, but sometimes the thumping of radiators made it less than quiet.

The winter of 1918 was mild but brought with it a serious 'flu epidemic that affected many families in the community. One of the nursing students remarked that "we more or less all finished up with the 'flu in 1918. It was a grilling ordeal for everyone. The nurses had to come on duty as soon as able or sooner, as we had several volunteer workers and could not accept more." Ruth Crump Caldwell recalls that her mother, Mrs. E.D. Crump, as well as Mrs. R.E. Harrison (Christine Musselman), and Mrs. Archer went to help with the nursing at the hospital. She goes on to say that, "All shopping done in Lamont, during the epidemic, was done from long tables outside of each of the stores in town. Everyone, while in a public place, was required to wear a gauze mask. These masks, at least in part, were distributed from my father's office on the main street of Lamont." The community clearly had to pull together to get through this very difficult time.

One of my early memories include the dirty, tobacco-stained face masks that were worn during the tragic flu epidemic in 1918 and 1919. These masks didn't seem to reduce the terrific toll of lives lost in our area, as some families were wiped out completely. My mother tells me that, during this epidemic, the school in Chipman was used for an infirmary or hospital. The regular hospitals were unable to cope with all of the people that were afflicted.

– Theodore and Gerald J. Krull

All hospital activities were of great importance and interest to the whole community. This was particularly true of the nurses' graduation exercises. We were allowed to leave school to attend this function. Some years school was closed for that afternoon.

– Nancy (Course) Sproul

Although there were only two graduates from the training program in the fall of 1918, there were three more in the spring of 1919. (There were no graduation exercises in 1920, due to the 1918 – 19 'flu epidemic, which caused delays in students completing their training.) Graduation had become an important event in the community. Friends and families of the graduates were all welcomed at the reception hosted by the doctor's wives, the other graduates and other community supporters. The graduation exercises were held in the church during the evening, although the church was often not large enough to accommodate all the well-wishers. As Florence Love says, "the warmth and friendliness shown by the community towards the doctors, nurses and the hospital was then, and still is, something unique."

LPH/AMH ALUMNAE COLLECTION

LPH Graduate Nurses, 1919
Left to right: Christine Campbell, Ruby Manton, Mary Peterman

Lamont Public Hospital had become a reality, from its inception only as a vision. Doctors, nurses, student nurses, families, community and church all contributed to the realization of that dream. Wood and paint were not the only things used to build this institution. Faith, skill, cooperation and compassion also formed the foundation on which it was built, firm characteristics which would continue to influence the growth of this hospital in the future.

LPH/AMH ALUMNAE COLLECTION

Lamont Public Hospital with 1921 changes

CHAPTER 3
1921 TO 1930
GROWING IN SERVICE

A growing number of patients from a wide radius around Lamont came to the Lamont Public Hospital for medical care, as word of its excellent doctors and exemplary care spread. By 1921, it had become apparent that renovations and an increase in the size of the hospital was necessary. The Board of Home Missions of the Methodist Church recognized the importance of serving a wider community and it paid the entire amount for renovations and additions – a total of $34,000.

1926 L.P.H. YEARBOOK

Nurses' Home, 1920's

There had been several women serve as Matron in the interval between Miss Musselman's departure in 1919 and Miss Welsh's arrival: Miss J. Peters, Miss Turner and Miss Evelyn Malloy. Other graduate nurses, from Lamont Hospital and other training schools, took on various responsibilities. Miss E. Malloy (Strathcona Hospital, Edmonton) was an assistant Matron and O.R. Supervisor; Miss Fannie Stafford (L.P.H. Class of '18) succeeded Miss Malloy as O.R. Supervisor, and was in turn succeeded by Miss Viola Kilgour (Calgary General Hospital); Miss Barbara Alexander came from the U.S.A. as an assistant to Miss Welsh, to be succeeded by Miss Helen P. Rice (Royal Victoria Hospital, Montreal).

The hospital was enlarged to officially provide 55 beds, although it did at times accommodate up to 65 patients. A new power plant was built to provide dependable heat and light, with electric generators and high pressure boilers. A third storey was added to provide more ward space. The front of the hospital was rebuilt, which gave more office space on the first floor and sunrooms to the other two floors.

The Nurses' Home also underwent a facelift. The Women's Missionary Society provided the funding needed to enlarge the building by eight more bedrooms which were added to the rear. A large veranda and balcony were added to the front. These additions meant that all the nursing staff could now be housed in one building for the first time.

In 1921, Lamont Public Hospital was granted approval under the standardized guidelines of The American College of Surgeons. Dr. Malcolm T. McEachern conducted the inspection, making Lamont the first Canadian hospital of 55 beds (outside of those in the cities) to receive this approval. Lamont has remained on the list of approved/accredited hospitals ever since.

THE LAMP IS GOLDEN

Miss Frances E. Welsh, Matron, 1921-1924

The staff of the hospital also continued to grow. Miss Frances Welsh came in January, 1921, to take over as Matron. Miss Welsh coordinated a more complete course offering for the student nurses, and was well-liked and respected for her ability as an instructress.

Dr. C.F. Connolly, who had been living at Pakan, then Andrew, before moving to Lamont, arrived in 1921 as the hospital's third doctor. (Early in 1922, he moved on and opened an office in Mundare, although he maintained his association with the Lamont Public Hospital for a time.) By 1921, there were eighteen student nurses, three graduate nurses and three doctors providing medical care in the hospital.

Support staff included Miss Edith Kellogg, the first cook at Lamont Hospital trained in dietetics; Mrs. E.J. Ralston (known as "Ma Ralston") who was housekeeper until 1926. Miss Annie Carson became the hospital's receptionist in 1922, and remained in this position until 1945.

Dr. M.A.R. Young, a recent graduate of McGill, arrived in 1922. He was to become the second "guiding hand" of Lamont Public Hospital, participating in its life for the next 56 years. In the 50th Anniversary history of the hospital (1962) Florence Love mentioned that Dr. Young attended his first graduation exercise of the School of Nursing in 1922, and "has been in attendance at all but one since then."

Five students of the 1920 and 1921 classes graduated together. In 1921, the University introduced examinations that graduate nurses had to write before they could become Registered Nurses. All members of the Class of '21 wrote these exams successfully.

The Class of 1922 was the largest to date. Nine graduates received their pins and diplomas on June 16, 1922, at a ceremony reported in the Edmonton Journal in which the "The Union Church... was crowded, standing room being at a premium." This class produced several firsts – the first missionary to go abroad (Ada Sandell), the first graduate nurse from L.P.H. to enter the Hospital Administration field (Helen Souder), the first L.P.H. nurse to receive two post graduate certificates (Mary McCallum), and the first nurse from L.P.H. to attend the Provincial Graduate Nurses' Association Convention (Florence McDonald).

1926 L.P.H. YEARBOOK

Dr. M.A.R. Young arrived in 1922

Morley Alphonso Ryerson Young was born December 17, 1894, on a farm in Manitoba. In 1915 he began medical studies at the University of Alberta, then went overseas with the First Canadian Tank Battalion. Upon his return to Canada he resumed his medical studies at McGill University in Montreal, Quebec, graduating in 1921. He did post-graduate work at the Montreal Maternity Hospital and Manitoba's Selkirk Mental Hospital before coming to Lamont, in 1922.

LPH/AMH ALUMNAE COLLECTION

Class of 1922. Back row: A. Bell, F. McDonald, A. Sandell, D. Spencer
Front row: A. Carson, M. McCallum, R. Sutherland, M. Sloane, H. Souder

May I say that my impression of the training of nurses at Lamont Public Hospital [is] that there is no other school that can compare to it for the service it renders and has rendered to the community, the province and the nation, to say nothing of what it has done for the Christian church, both in Canada and other lands... I am proud of my alma mater and and humbly pay this tribute to it.

– Ada Sandell

1926 L.P.H. YEARBOOK

Dr. Jack Alton, 1923

During this time, Dr. Archer was actively extending his sphere of influence in the hospital field. He was a speaker at the "First Convention of the Hospitals in the Province of Alberta" in 1919, addressing the convention on the subject of "The Function of a Small Hospital in the Community". He became president of the Alberta Hospital Association for the 1920-1921 term, and President of the Alberta Medical Association during 1921-1922. In 1921, he also received a Fellowship in the American College of Surgeons, in recognition of his abilities as a surgeon.

Dr. (John) Jack Alton became associated with the hospital in the spring of 1923. He had practiced at Waskatenau for a number of years, before coming to Lamont with his family. He specialized in caring for children and maternity patients at the hospital, and developed a reputation as a fine doctor in this capacity. It was not until 34 years later that he would retire from this role.

Miss Helen Rice replaced Miss Welsh as Superintendent of Nurses in 1924, when Miss Welsh took a position at the new Isolation Hospital in Edmonton. Miss Mary McCallum, Class of '22, became the assistant and Miss Augusta Riske, Class of '23, was Operating Room Supervisor.

1926 L.P.H. YEARBOOK

Miss Helen Rice,
Superintendent of Nurses,
1924-1930

FROM BUSH TO BUSHELS

The doctors used different styles of transportation to make "house calls". In the photo below, Dr. Archer (left) stands beside "The Bug", a 1924 Ford cut down by Mike Kroening to the width of a sleigh track. Alex Mitchell (above left) and George Viteychuk (above right) stand beside a snowmobile, built by Paul Hrycyk, for the doctors' use.

ALONG VICTORIA TRAIL

In May, 1924, the Student Nurses' Association of Lamont Public Hospital was fully organized. It had come into being in 1921 with a President and Secretary-Treasurer, but no formal constitution. Meetings were held at irregular times, because of the unpredictability of duty hours. By 1924, the constitution had been approved and enacted by the students and faculty. There is an interesting note in the 1926 yearbook that tells more about this process and the people involved. The nurses were feeling their inexperience and need of support so they thought it would be most expedient if they used a system of government similar to that of secondary schools, in which the activities were carefully monitored by members of the faculty. It goes on to say that "Our Faculty, however, refused to consider this form, insisting that the girls be deemed capable of conducting their own affairs, and that only an independent form of Student government would be adopted... We felt grateful to our Faculty for the tribute they had paid us and by the same token felt a challenge to use our utmost ability in conducting student affairs in such a way as to warrant their confidence."

A memorable experience occurred in the early part of 1924, when I was on night duty. I witnessed the first dose of insulin being administered in the Lamont Public Hospital, to a diabetic patient who was brought into the hospital in a diabetic coma. Dr. Archer and Dr. Young administered the medication and the patient made a most remarkable return to consciousness. Dr. Archer exclaimed in a whisper, "Its a miracle, its a miracle!"

– Eleanor (Palmer) Cleary, Class of '24

THE LAMP IS GOLDEN

Doctors and their wives, 1925

The relationship of the faculty and students was clearly a special one. This was demonstrated in 1925, when a question was put to the nursing students whether to admit Asian women to the School of Nursing. In a secret ballot vote, the students unanimously voted in favor. Chio Kubo and Grace Oyama were admitted in 1925, and were thought to be the first admitted to a school of nursing in Canada. Over the years, 22 students of Chinese, Japanese, or Korean origin have graduated from Lamont.

The Methodist and Presbyterian Churches underwent amalgamation in 1925, becoming the United Church of Canada. The hospital continued to be operated under the auspices of this new merger, under the newly formed Home Mission Board of the United Church. Additional renovations were undertaken to the hospital and Nurses' Home. A third floor was added to the Nurses' Home, alleviating congestion in that building. An elevator was installed in the hospital, hand powered at first, but later changed to electric, with push-button control.

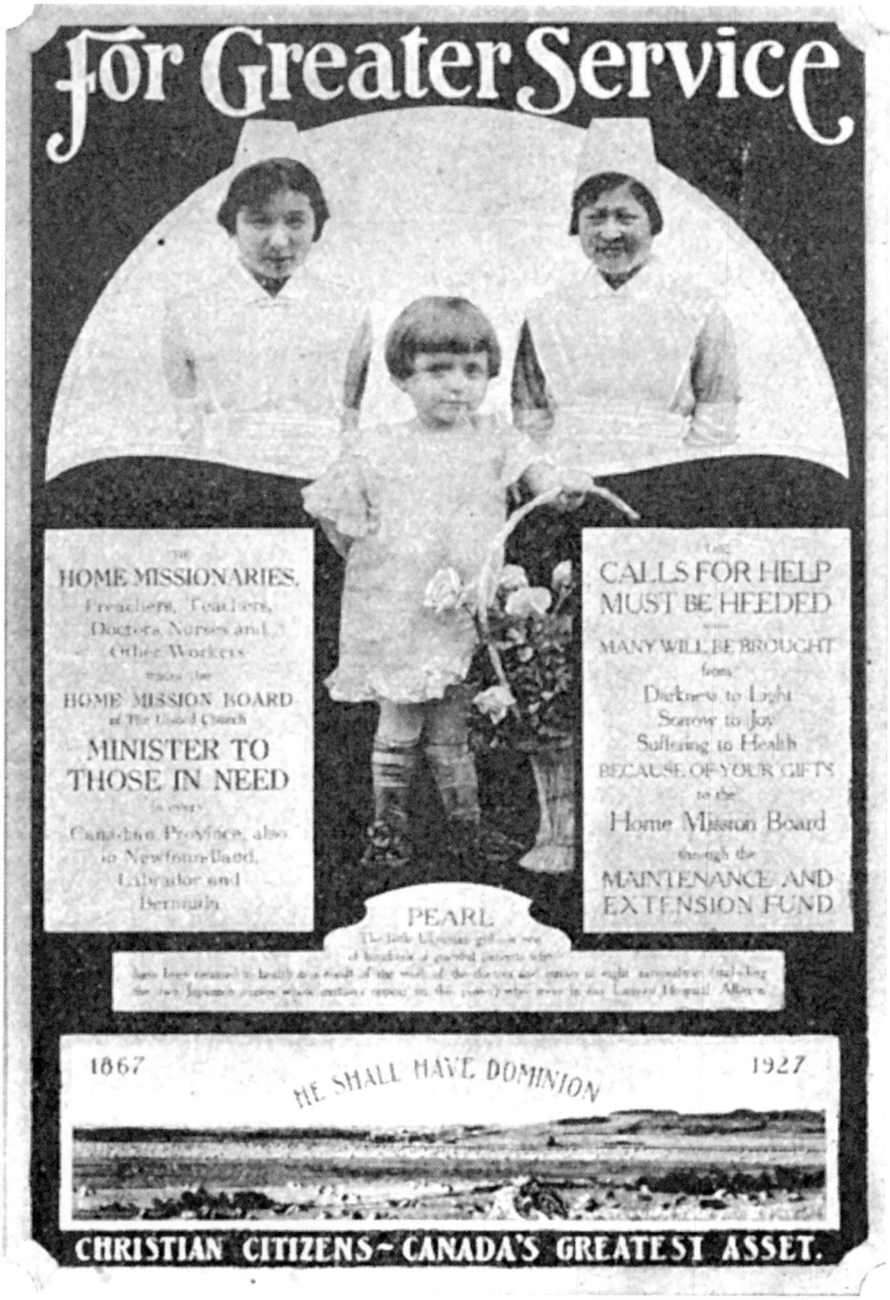

The reputation of Lamont Hospital continued to grow, right alongside all the structural changes. In a leaflet produced by the Home Mission Board of the United Church, dated 1926, glimpses of that increasing reputation can be found. It states that, "The faith in the doctor's skill is rather miraculous. One woman said 'Oh yes, I tell you, we just swear by Dr. Archer and the rest. Dr. Archer can always do something if it is possible at all to do it.' One of the nurses said with a gay grimace, 'We had a Russian the other day who said he wanted to come here because he knew we had good tools.'"

UNITED CHURCH MISSION LEAFLET

Poster, Home Mission Board

UNITED CHURCH MISSION LEAFLET

Nurses of eight countries of origin were in attendance at Lamont Public Hospital's School of Nursing. From left to right, top row: Chiyo Kubo, Japanese; Grace Oyama, Japanese; Inez Fenton, Canadian; Catherine Sandergarth, Danish; Elsi Ayers, English; Helen Lakusta, Ruthenian; Left to right, bottom row: Helen MacDonald, Scottish Canadian; Elsie Aronson, Swedish; Miss Hennig, German

7:30 a.m. Six nurses with heaping laundry baskets, wend their way up several flights of creaking stairways. Pausing at each turn long enough to replenish their failing air supply, and to dream a hopeless dream of future ease. BUT WAIT! – Long weeks of construction result in a masterpiece consisting of a moving platform, propelled by means of ropes. Orders are issued that no pupil nurse be allowed to run elevator. Orders obeyed to the letter – i.e. 7:30 a.m. finds six nurses still wending their weary way upstairs with heaping laundry baskets. Weeks pass. More construction work. At last our dreams are realized. Electricity is installed and the elevator becomes a reality. Nurses are found joy-riding and a death penalty imposed, but only for a short time. We now have full-swing, i.e. – unless we are riding from basement to third floor with a mere excuse of step-saving.

– 1926 L.P.H. Yearbook

Lamont Public Hospital was unique in other ways. The same Mission leaflet drew attention to the fact that Lamont was a centre where differences in nationality were celebrated. At one point eight nationalities were represented by nurses graduated from or training at the training school, quite an accomplishment for such a small hospital.

The story of the children associated with this hospital continues, too, with the story of Little Pearl, mentioned in this same leaflet. Pearl Blazenko was discovered by Dr. Archer while visiting her home where a sibling was sick with a fever. Pearl was a victim of rickets and had no strength in her limbs to carry her or to hold things in her hands. He persuaded the family to let him take Pearl to the hospital, where she spent a year and nine months. At the graduation exercises of the hospital that June, Pearl was a very happy and proud flower girl sharing the special day with her caregivers.

UNITED CHURCH MISSION LEAFLET

Little Pearl, centre, as flower girl at graduation, 1926

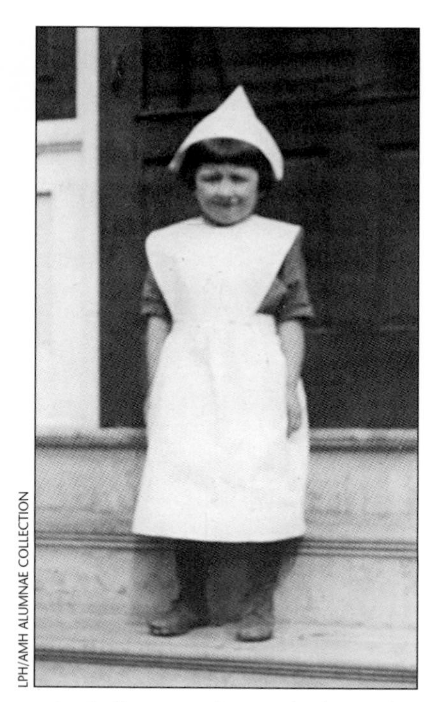

LPH/AMH ALUMNAE COLLECTION

Annie Goyan, patient at the hospital, 1922-1930

Another child whose life was interwoven in the life of the hospital for a number of years was Annie Goyan. Suffering from diphtheria, Annie was given the medical treatment known as a "tracheotomy" to facilitate her breathing. She spent many years at the hospital in the care of the doctors and nurses and was finally able to return to her home near Smoky Lake in 1930.

The work of the hospital touched many lives. In the 1925/26 year, there were 398 surgical cases, 86 obstetrical, 779 medical, a total of 1263 admissions. The number of out-patients was 1364. Doctors Archer, Rush, Alton and Connolly formed the basis for the development of the Lamont Clinic in 1925, a form of group practice that is still in effect today at Lamont.

Dr. Rush began to look towards retirement in 1926, and his position as Secretary-Treasurer was taken over by the Reverend C.W.W. Ross. Reverend Ross acted as the Chaplain to the hospital during this time as well. He and his wife played another important role in the life of the hospital, as this quote from Florence Love reveals, "Mr. and Mrs. Ross' home was open to the student nurses in their hours off duty; a haven, when loneliness and home-sickness, a disease often found among the younger nurses, overtook them."

SUMMO COMMISSO MISSI, the motto of the Nurses' Training School at Lamont, was Latin for "On Highest Mission Sent". Its origins are not clear from available sources (it has been suggested it originated with Dr. Archer). It was used as early as 1916 on the pins given at graduation. The first yearbook in 1926 featured on the cover the L.H.P. logo with Summo Commisso Missi, a reminder of the ever-present guiding principles of the Lamont Public Hospital School of Nursing.

The student nurses partially developed their sense of family and belonging through the first year book, produced in 1926 at a cost of $100.00 for the 52 page book. The introductory editorial reads "Acting upon an impulse, created by a sense of growing power, and a desire to see our school ranked among larger institutions, we undertook that which heretofore our predecessors have been unable to present – a year book." Filled with the usual photos of graduating students, anecdotes, and humorous quips, it gives some insight into the nurses' lives while they were in training.

1928 L.H.P. YEARBOOK

Reverend C.W.W. Ross, served as Chaplain and Secretary-Treasurer

For example, the students all took part in a play that was presented to the public on March 27, 1925, called "Perplexing Situations". It was, by all accounts, a social and financial success. The 1927 yearbook cites the play of that year as "Whose Little Bride Are You?" Among several humorous offstage notes: "Mr. Stewart had some difficulty converting nurses into men of all ages, from real young ones to old dissipated ones. Saddest of all – there was no curtain between the ladies and gents dressing rooms."

A new form of public recognition came for the graduating nurses of 1926 and 1927, with the introduction of awards to members of the graduating class. Daisy Young, Class of '26, was awarded a five dollar gold coin by Miss F.E. Welsh, for general proficiency. Alma Ross received the Gold Medal for Proficiency in 1927. The Elizabeth Young Memorial Prize was first offered in 1927, presented by Dr. M.A.R. Young in memory of his mother. Its first recipient was Vernice Young.

The School of Nursing received a boost in 1927/28 with the addition of teaching facilities which were made available by a new addition built at this time. A lecture room and demonstration area on the third floor of the old building could now be used for lectures, as well as a library and study area.

The Home Mission Board once again provided the funding, (a total of $26,000) for the 1928 addition. A new stucco and brick building with a full basement was added to the east side of the original hospital building, and was connected to it by hallways. The upper storey was built as private ward and contained seven private rooms, with all the modern facilities of the times. The lower floor was made into offices, three of which the medical staff rented, along with a waiting room and receptionist's desk. The Training School Office and a room for a new X-ray machine were also on that floor. The basement, which was at ground level, housed a dentist's office, intern's quarters and a modern laundry facility (until it was relocated to a separate building). The place the laundry occupied briefly was later remodelled to accommodate the offices of the Lamont Health Unit.

Ada Sandell, Class of '22, became a missionary to Korea, where she spent 36 years of her life devoted the health and well-being of the Korean people. Vera Boyd, Class of '28, became the second graduate to enter the mission field. She was posted in central India in 1930, served several communities for 34 years, and was awarded the Kaiser-I-Hind Medal, a very high honour bestowed by the British Government. Florence E.C. Reid, Class of '27, devoted her life to work at the Red Cross Crippled Children's Hospital in Calgary, Alberta, for which she received Calgary's Outstanding Citizen Award in 1953.

1928 L.P.H. YEARBOOK

Lamont Public Hospital, 1928

In November, 1928, Dr. Rush and his wife left Lamont for Vancouver, British Columbia, to enjoy retirement. In a letter to the graduates of 1928, Dr. Rush said, "As I look back over the years I can see better than you can how this Institution has grown and improved until it is now second to nothing in its size anywhere that I know. Lamont nurses have every reason to be proud of their Training School."

THE LAMP IS GOLDEN

Miss Louil Wright, Superintendent of Nurses, 1930-1939

Other staff changes occurred over the next two years. Dr. M. Mallett of Mundare became associated with the hospital in 1930, after working with Dr. Connolly in Mundare for some time. Miss Rice resigned her position as Superintendent of Nurses in 1930, to take a position in Montreal. She was succeeded by the first graduate of Lamont Public Hospital's School of Nursing to take the position of Superintendent of Nurses – Miss Louil Wright, a graduate of the Class of '27. Miss Agnes McLeod, a graduate of the University of Alberta, became the first qualified instructress at Lamont Public Hospital. She was followed by Miss Ruth Thompson.

LPH/AMH ALUMNAE COLLECTION

Dr. M. Mallett arrived 1930

Lamont Public Hospital certainly had grown over the years between 1921 and 1930. In a financial report published in 1929, statistics were cited as follows: admissions – 1705, out-patients – 2364, hospital days – 20 361, cost per patient per day – $3.10, births – 136. Lamont Public Hospital was becoming well known as a small but highly effective hospital. The combination of a functional physical facility, excellence in medical care, and strong Christian values provided an opportunity for many to serve in ways that were personally meaningful. "Summo Commisso Missi" (On Highest Mission Sent) became a strong theme for not only the training school at Lamont, but also for the many individuals whose lives were influenced by the hospital.

1931 L.H.P. YEARBOOK

The faculty at Lamont Public Hospital, 1931. Top row (left to right): Dr. Alton, Dr. Mallett, Dr. Archer, Dr. Webber
Bottom row (left to right): Dr. Young, Miss R. Thompson, Miss L. Wright, Mrs. R. Shears, Mr. C.W.W. Ross

CHAPTER 4
1931 TO 1940
CONTINUING TRADITIONS

Throughout the years of the Depression, when the country was caught in the grip of scarcity, Lamont Public Hospital retained a degree of stability that enabled it to continue meeting the needs of the community it served. One of the important factors contributing to that stability was the team of people who held positions of leadership and responsibility.

Dr. Archer, Dr. Young, and Dr. Alton, plus the junior doctors and our wonderful lady superintendent, Miss. H. Rice, and Miss Alma Ross, the operating room superintendent, all made us nurses who could take our place anywhere, as many have done.

– Elva M. (Yeates) Ferrier, Class of '29

Dr. Archer, Dr. Young, Dr. Mallett, and Dr. Alton were joined in their work by Miss Louil Wright, Superintendent of Nurses, Miss Ruth Thompson, Instructress, and Mrs. R. Shears, O.R. Supervisor. Dr. Webber, a dentist and Reverend C.W.W. Ross, Hospital Chaplain and Secretary-Treasurer, contributed other important skills. This strong team of professionals provided the anchor that held throughout these challenging years.

The 1931 yearbook stated that "There have been no startling changes during the past year, but an ever progressive renewal of paint and plaster makes us feel sure that we are not slipping back." Records show that the hospital cared for 1581 patients with a total of 19 036 hospital days in 1932, with the added comment that "This year has been unusually busy, at times crowded to more than capacity."

The changes that did occur over this time were always modest, often small matters that made a big difference. For example, the nurses' uniform underwent another change when Louise Anthony wore a uniform with short sleeves "to test the change and if possible obtain the doctor's approval." The doctors apparently approved, because short sleeves have been a part of the uniform ever since, to everyone's greater comfort.

ALONG VICTORIA TRAIL

Lamont Public Hospital, 1931

THE LAMP IS GOLDEN

First Alumnae Luncheon, 1932

The 1931 graduation saw the birth of a new body, the Alumnae Association. Since the inception of the training program, there had been a total of 84 nurses graduate from the hospital at Lamont. Although the nurses were now spread far and wide, there was great interest in and support for an Alumnae Association. The Association, in Florence Love's words, "has tried to promote understanding in the profession and ethical conduct at all times. It has ever looked forward and has been of help to graduates and students by the many projects it has undertaken." One of the Alumnae Association's special events was initiated in 1932, when a luncheon for the graduates was put on by the Association. This has since become an annual event, celebrating the graduating class.

Maria Boutillier, Class of '31, was installed as the first President of the Alumnae Association and was supported by Miss Louil Wright (Class of '27) as Vice President, Daisy (Young) Craig, (Class of '26) as Secretary-Treasurer, and Florrie Reid (Class of '27) as the correspondence secretary and editor of the newsletter. Mrs. R.E. Harrison, Honorary President, and four Honorary members, Miss Welsh, Miss Rice, Mrs. Archer and Mrs. Young, completed the executive.

THE LAMP IS GOLDEN

Maria Boutillier,
first Alumnae Association President

Dr. Archer, wearing one of his awards, with Miss Louil Wright and Miss Ruth Thompson

Also in 1931, the Royal College of Physicians and Surgeons of Canada was initiated by an Act of Parliament. Prior to this, it had been necessary for doctors to go to Britain for study and examination, to receive their Fellowship in the Royal College. With the creation of the new Canadian College, Dr. Archer was able to add the letters F.R.C.S (C) after his name.

Noreen Lum, a graduate of the Class of '32, went on to nurse at Happy Valley Hospital in Hong Kong, where she remained as Superintendent of Nurses throughout four years of Japanese occupation. Catherine Stewart, Class of '35 went overseas during the war, with the Red Cross Orthopedic and Plastic Surgery Unit, working as a ward and operating room nurse.

Dr. Archer continued to be influential in medical circles. He was a member of the Council of the College of Physicians and Surgeons of Alberta for many years, and was its President in 1930, 1931, and 1936. He was instrumental in preparing a submission to the first council on the provision of medical services for all people of Alberta. His activities in the medical profession earned him the honour of O.B.E. (Officer of the Order of the British Empire) in 1936.

In addition to his medical pursuits, Dr. Archer found time to be involved in the community. He served on the school board, was on the Town council, and acted as Mayor. He was a member of the Mission Board of the United Church of Canada, and an elder in the local church. Both he and Mrs. Archer taught Sunday school and sang in the choir.

Dr. Young also was involved in the community, with the Young People's Society (Y.P.S.), associated with the United Church. Dr. Young said, "The ten Depression years of the nineteen thirties constituted two thirds of the life time of the Y.P.S. It was a time when you provided locally most of your local activities and entertainment." Membership began at about twenty, grew to over sixty, then averaged forty to forty five.

ALONG VICTORIA TRAIL

Young People's Society, 1927

The group participated in discussions, debates, musical events, art exhibits, had speakers and went on outings, like skating parties and sleigh rides. The editors of several yearbooks remarked on the importance of the Y.P.S. to the life of the nurses, how many of them were members, and how much the outings were enjoyed.

There was humour and comraderie during these lean years, as people turned to each other, their institution and their community to create a rich life together. In the 1931 yearbook, an article entitled "Our Student Government Rules" (which would normally be a serious list of do's and don'ts) advises nurses, tongue-in-cheek, that "When nurses find themselves, or their belongings, thrown over the fence, they may consider that they have received notice to quit." Or, "All nurses are requested to rise at 6 a.m. This is imperative as the sheets are needed for tablecloths."

The 1933 yearbook stands out from all the others. There was no financing available for the yearbook that year, but the committee continued on undaunted, creating a book of 43 pages for each graduate. It was prepared on a shoestring budget for ditto copying, without the usual nice cover and glossy pages. It does, however, include the traditional "bequeaths" that began with the first yearbook, in which the graduating class determines their "last wishes" for all members of the faculty and nursing school. Its freehand drawings and handwritten entries by faculty and participants makes it a fresh read, even after all these years.

1937 L.H.P. YEARBOOK

One of the many plays put on by the student nurses was "Here Comes Charlie", in 1937

LHP/AMH ALUMNAE COLLECTION

Tennis Courts

Our tennis champs spent many hours on the court and they certainly play the game! A court for basketball was laid out for our further enjoyment last summer and Limestone Lake players suffered considerably in the hands of the hefty Lamont Basket Winners. Dr. Mallett is an exceptionally good shot and we hope he keeps up the good work.
– 1940 yearbook

The nurses enjoyed the social benefits of extra-curricular activities, such as a Literary Review Club, started in 1937, with Mrs. A. Wiltze (Alberta Reeves, Class of '38) as its first President. A tennis court was available for the nurses for several years, and a basketball court was set up later until the space was needed for other things. The custom of an annual play continued, with such presentations as "Betty's Last Bet" (1932) and "Here Comes Charlie" (1937). The corn roast parties were legendary, along with swimming or skating parties at Elk Island Park, and other holiday events at Halloween or Valentine's. Nursing students could not always afford to make it home for Christmas but that, too, was looked after. "On Christmas Eve thirty-two stockings hung by the fireplace. Santa Claus was good to all of us. In spite of qualms of homesickness, everyone went to bed feeling that there were worse places in which to spend Christmas Eve than L.P.H." (1937 yearbook).

The hospital staff were saddened to learn of the death of Dr. Rush, in October, 1935. A tribute in the 1936 yearbook reads in part, "We remember him with gratitude and pride; gratitude for his unfailing friendship and fidelity, and pride in his personal and professional distinction. A warm personal friend has left us, and every member of our staff and every alumna of the Training School will want to pause again in their busy lives and remember him with gratitude and affection."

ALONG VICTORIA TRAIL

Reverend C.W.W. Ross, about 1935

Another long time member of the hospital staff, Reverend C.W.W. Ross, Secretary-Treasurer and Hospital Chaplain, left Lamont in 1936 to continue his ministry work in Smoky Lake. The nursing school held a farewell tea in honor of Mr. and Mrs. Ross, who had played such an important role in the lives of so many nurses. There were fond reminiscences of the Sunday Afternoon Song Service started by Reverend and Mrs. Ross. A portable organ was brought to the hospital each Sunday and the nurses, patients, visitors and students would sing for 20 to 30 minutes, between shift change. Even after the Ross family left, this tradition carried on, as it meant so much to both nurses and patients. Reverend Ross touched many lives during his work at Lamont Hospital. His role as Hospital Chaplain was taken over by the minister of the United Church and it would remain so until the early 1950's.

From the business office records, we have figures for the 1936 year of operation. These include the usual list of admissions (1760) and out-patients (6653), along with a few other notes of interesting trivia. Meals served numbered 115 500, the number of loaves of bread used was 12 178, and the number of tons of coal used amounted to 1440. The average number of employees had grown to 55 and the total cost of operation for the year was $50,639.89.

The "Ten Commandments for Nurses of L.P.H." was a feature item in the yearbook of 1932. Among the dictums were these gems: Thou shalt not make any date with the patients, Thou shalt not take the name of the faculty in vain, Honor the rules of thy school and uphold thy hospital technique that thy days in training might not be prolonged, Thou shalt not eat late lunches more than seven times a week, Six days shalt thou labor and on the seventh one thou shalt have long hours.

ALONG VICTORIA TRAIL

Union Church fire, January 20, 1936

On January 20, 1936, a fire of unknown origin started in the Union Church, destroying the building and contents. The building of the new church represented a true expression of community cooperation and involvement. With building materials in short supply, stones were hauled in from the surrounding fields and the church was built with the labour of every faith and nationality in the local area. The interior woodwork was exquisitely executed by an artist from Edmonton, a Major Norbury. Frank Rupchyk, a stone mason working on the church, would not make a church without a cross, so he worked several light colored stones into the shape of a cross in the bell tower, to meet his own requirement. The first nursing class to graduate from "The Stone Church" was that of 1937.

LHP/AMH ALUMNAE COLLECTION

Construction of new United Church, 1936

[June] is now completely cured, able to run and play and enjoy life almost equally as well as any normal child of her age, thanks to the untiring patience and skill of the doctors and nurses.

– C.W.W. Ross

Children continued to be an important part of those who were in-patients. The United Church Record and Missionary Review, February, 1935 edition, featured stories about two of the hospital's special children, known as Little June and Little Peter. June Warriner had been born with severely clubbed feet. She was admitted to the hospital July 3, 1929, at the age of two weeks and stayed almost five years. She was operated on to correct the problem and then put in casts which were changed frequently to accommodate the slow changes that were part of the straightening process. Finally, she wore a shoe with a support and was completely cured by the time she left the hospital to rejoin her family, on June 28, 1935.

Peter Yakimishyn was admitted to the hospital on August 2, 1933, at the age of nine months. He was born born with a prominent facial birthmark that was overgrown with hair. Treatment consisted of applications of liquid carbon dioxide, which was administered very carefully so as not to destroy the underlying tissue, leaving a scar. "Peter is a very bright and sweet little boy, and the missionary doctors hope to be able to send him out in life with a clear, clean countenance. He is the product of a very poor home, and were it not for the kindly Christian doctors whose main objects in life are to render service, and for a missionary institution, this would not be at all possible."

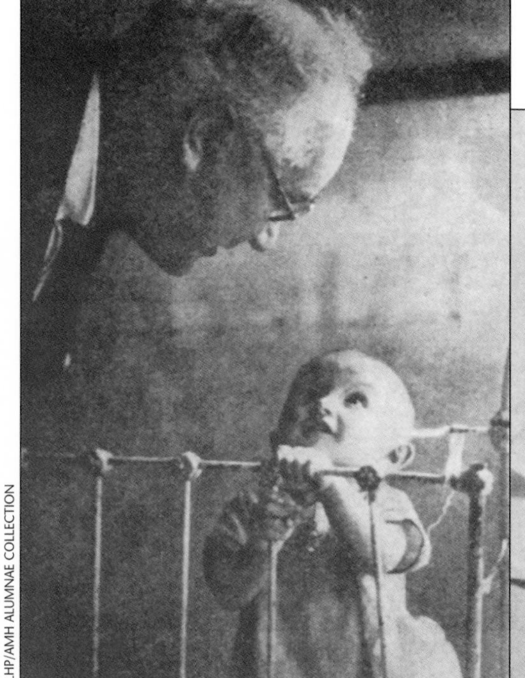

LHP/AMH ALUMNAE COLLECTION

Little June with C.W.W. Ross

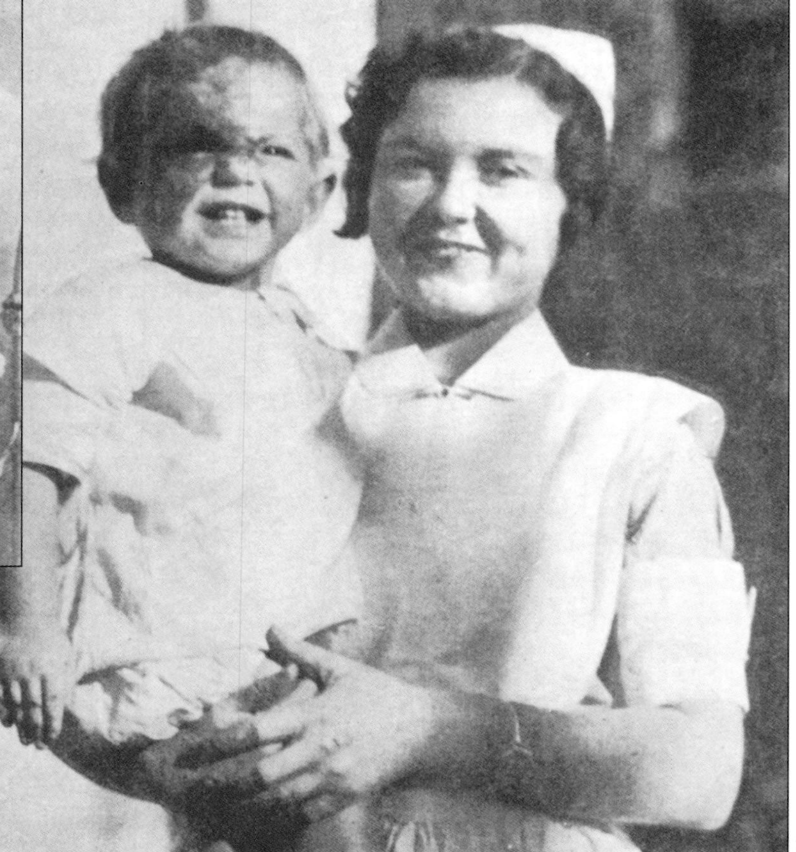

LHP/AMH ALUMNAE COLLECTION

Little Peter with nurse Isabelle Hannah

1937 L.H.P. YEARBOOK

Hospital with addition, 1937

This "missionary institution" was to undergo yet another renovation to increase its functionality. The Board of Home Missions of the United Church, an on-going presence in the life of this hospital, facilitated many of the improvements and alterations over the years. In 1937, the space between the original frame building and the newer stucco structure was filled in, resulting in changes on each floor. The basement now accommodated the dispensary, which meant a change in the nurses' dining room. On the first floor, there were changes to the business office, main entrance and waiting room. The house doctor's room took up the spare space on the second floor, and a new classroom came into being on the third floor. The old classroom became a sunroom which was much appreciated by the younger patients of the hospital.

A summary of statistics for 1938 inform us that the hospital now had 80 beds (7 private, 16 semi-private, 41 ward, 8 bassinettes, and 8 cots). Fifty one of the beds were designated as medical and surgical, 8 were obstetrical, 8 nursery, 8 pediatrics, and 5 tuberculosis. Obstetrical cases numbered 156, with two still births. Men's surgical cases were 266, women's, 246. Men's medical cases numbered 505, and women, 664. The hospital was obviously fulfilling a great need in its day-to-day functioning.

In 1938, the Alberta Government opened a Department of Public Health Unit, with the administrative office in Lamont. Housed on the lower floor of the hospital, it was staffed by a doctor, three nurses, a dentist and clerical staff.

It wasn't just any one person, any one lecture, any one patient, the little town or district, that could have been accredited with the sum total of success in the Lamont Grad's life. It was the unified whole of one community, working collectively toward the betterment of human health and welfare. The moral status, the discipline, the intellectual pool, that overwhelming sense of goodwill that permeated the corridors of Lamont Public Hospital... were the very fibres that scatter [ed] each one of us throughout the globe, to function in our individual capacities, with an awareness of humanism that challenges words to seek definition.

– Norma (Manuel) Kier, Class of '36

1940 L.H.P. YEARBOOK

Miss Olga Scheie,
1939-1940

THE LAMP IS GOLDEN

Miss M. Wallace,
1940-1941

Norah McCallum, Class of '39, took additional training through the University of Alberta, obtaining her B.Sc. degree, as well as a post graduate course in Obstetrics from the Vancouver General Hospital. She then went on to Public Health work in the Peace River area, and in the southern part of the province, under the Communicable Diseases Branch of the Government of Alberta.

The municipality funded one half its costs, and the remaining portion was covered by the provincial government. Its main role was to educate and offer public health services to the area's population, through such activities as school visits, clinics, dental care, and poster/essay contests for school children emphasizing good health practices. Preventive health care services were now working in tandem with doctors and hospital services, and "were making a great difference to the people of this and neighboring municipalities" according to the 1938 yearbook.

On several occasions there were suggestions that this merger of services was an innovative move. Dr. Young said, "The close association of those interested in preventative medicine and those carrying out the treatment aspects presents a very interesting and useful experiment."

ALONG VICTORIA TRAIL

Office staff: Kae Scraba, Norman Archer, Annie Ross, Murray Ross, Helen Perrich, Bill Williams, Gwen Shears, Grace Wilson, Findlay Ross, 1938

Once the shadow of the Depression had lifted, changes in staff begin to occur. Miss M. Lipsey arrived in 1937 as a graduate dietitian and completely revamped the program in that department. Mr. Murray Ross came as the hospital's first official business manager. Miss L. Wright resigned her position as Superintendent of Nurses to be married, and was replaced by another graduate of Lamont Hospital, Olga Scheie who stayed for a year before she, too, left to be married. In 1940, Miss Margaret Wallace, a graduate of the Winnipeg General Hospital, came as Superintendent of Nurses.

It was a challenge during the 1930's to maintain the traditions of outstanding medical care that had been established at Lamont Public Hospital. However, under the guidance of exceptional staff and with the support of the United Church, the hospital was able to weather these times. The community's willingness to embrace the hospital as their own, and the vitality of the training school added a warm human touch to the institution. All of these elements, as well as the changing social and political backdrop of medical care in Alberta, continued Lamont Public Hospital's evolution.

1972 A.M.H. YEARBOOK

Dr. Archer at work

CHAPTER 5
1941 TO 1950

END OF AN ERA

Speaking to the graduates of 1931, Dr. Archer summed up his abiding faith and vision that a hospital could be more than just simply a place to receive medical help. "The Soul of a hospital is the spirit which infuses life into its material functions. Its soul consists of the spirit that pervades it, the morale of its workers, their intellectual and spiritual condition and attitude, the motives that impel them and the attitude they take to their work. This soul, the spiritual content of the Hospital – the essential characteristics which constitute the real institution – is of vital importance. It is independent of material wealth and expensive surroundings and is of vastly greater significance."

Dr. Archer was also a visionary in other ways. Access to medical care for all people had been a concern of his for many years. During the 1930's Depression, there were many people who could not afford to pay for the hospital's care. At that time there was no hospital insurance plan, and governments waffled on who should be responsible for the "indigent" (the poor). The government finally required the municipalities to cover a portion of the costs of the indigent and the idea of hospital contracts was born. In 1933, Lamont entered into an agreement with the District of Wostock to cover the medical payments of 4500 people using the five doctors. The program was severely overused and therefore not financially successful for the first two years of operation. However, by 1938, four other municipalities wanted to participate in the plan to extend the coverage to 18 000 people under 14 doctors. This larger plan never materialized, but the village of Andrew did join. The Alberta Act was in part, modelled after these contracts and the seeds of universal access to medical care were sown with these early experiments.

Dr. Archer was instrumental in bringing awareness of these needs into a much wider arena. He became the President of the Canadian Medical Association in 1942, and later served as consultant in medical economics for the CMA. His expertise and knowledge were a great asset during these times of planning and development of health care programs. Dr. Archer's work within the medical profession earned him the distinction of Commander of the Order of the British Empire (C.B.E.) in 1942, and the honorary degree of LLD. from both the Universities of Manitoba and Alberta.

LHP/AMH ALUMNAE COLLECTION

Dr. Archer's Liberal Candidacy, 1945

Dr. Archer was persuaded by Prime Minister William Lyon MacKenzie King to run as a Liberal candidate in support of medicare. However it seemed his constituents had other ideas; it is reported that he lost this political bid because the local community did not want to lose him, so they voted for someone else.

1972 A.M.H. YEARBOOK

Lamont Public Hospital
in the 1940's

The war cast a shadow on practically everything during our training years. One of the girls in our class received roses for her graduation from a boy who had been 'missing in action' for several weeks. He had ordered them early. We all had brothers, cousins, friends or sweethearts overseas, and the war news was very grim those three years.

– Vera (Coristine) Halvarson,
Class of '43

ALONG VICTORIA TRAIL

Gwen Burke, Grace Wilson, Annie Ross, Lois Easton,
Cassie Woycenko, office staff, 1944

During the War Years, there was rationing and supplies were scarce, however, the staff continued to offer the highest quality of care possible, even with the uncertainty and limitations of war-time. Office staff grew and continued to provide the support necessary to run the hospital's business affairs. Dr. M.A.R. Young took on increasing responsibility for the operation of the training school. Miss Wallace continued as Superintendent of Nurses until 1942 when Miss Ada Sandell (Class of '22), who had returned as an instructress for a short time, took over. (During this period, Miss Sandell was on loan from the Women's Missionary Society of the United Church of Canada, until conditions warranted her return to the overseas mission fields.) Another staff change saw Dr. M. Mallett relocate to Edmonton around 1942.

1945 A.M.H. YEARBOOK

Miss Sandell, Instructress and
Superintendent of Nurses, 1941-1945

The purpose of the I Eta Pie sorority started in 1941 was, in one nurse's words, "To get together and eat." In a much more formal document that has been retained in the Alumnae archives we are informed that "Our Purpose Shall Be to "Et" all manner of etables in the form of pies, cakes, toast, raw onion sandwiches and such worthy culinary successes or failures that come within our vision. And so Down with the scales, Long live the cooks."

– Magnus Carter of the I Eta Pie Sorority

Throughout the years 1940-1945, there were several events and people that left their mark on the hospital. Nurses continued to arrive and depart from the training school and the 1941 class was the largest to receive their pins and diplomas. This class also achieved fame with the development of the I Eta Pie sorority that began during their stay at Lamont.

Reverend Anson Moorehouse and staff of the Audio-Visual department of the United Church of Canada produced a film that depicted the early days of the hospital at Lamont. Many of the original people played themselves in the film, "Western Hands are Sure", which captures a feeling for the early struggles and later growth of the Lamont Public Hospital.

1972 A.M.H. YEARBOOK

Class of '41, the largest to date

Two new awards were given in the 1940's to deserving graduates. In addition to the Gold Medal for General Proficiency, awarded by the Hospital Board, and the Elizabeth Young Memorial presented by Dr. M.A.R. Young, the Ann Egglesfield Sinclair Prize for the "highest aggregate in Theory in the first four pre-clinical months" was first given in 1947. Mrs. Sinclair had been a member of the Class of '21. An Intermediate Proficiency Award was also first given in 1949 to the student showing the most progress in her intermediate year. Verna Dewhirst was that recipient.

There is story that a man "finally graduated from the Lamont Hospital", although he was not in the nursing profession. In 1944, Barrie E. Cooper began training at Lamont Public Hospital as a radiology technician, under Dr. Mallett and Joan Graham, R.N.R.T. He was then registered in Alberta and worked under Dr. Robert Bell until 1948. He married Mary Tokaruk, Class of '43.

Walter Serediak, another young patient at the hospital, suffered from a curvature of the spine. He was ferried to and from school by Ross Shears on a little sleigh through the winter months. His Grade two teacher shared that since Walter was unable to sit at his desk, he stood beside it to accomplish his work. Peter Yakimishyn (Little Peter) was still a resident at the hospital as well. Walter and Peter became good friends and could be found playing together on many occasions.

ALONG VICTORIA TRAIL

Walter Serediak and Peter Yakimishyn, 1939

Some of the nurses were housed in a different residence during the early to mid 1940's, as student numbers increased but the space to house them had not. The old "Stone House" was mentioned by several of the nursing students of this time. This building just west of the hospital, built of the same cinder blocks as Dr. Archer's second home in 1910, was originally the residence for the Presbyterian minister. It was very sparsely furnished and cold in the winter, as there were no trees or storm windows to break the northwest winds. Water and heat were always a problem but somehow the nurses managed.

Jean McPhee, Class of '43, reminisced, "Three of us started residence in the stone house west of the hospital which is now owned by Mr. and Mrs. Roy Carter. The occupants included seven students and one instructor, Miss Brown, and her cat. Our duties included checking the furnace and pumping water up to a tank on the second floor so that we could have running water. Sometimes we got over-ambitious and over-flowed the tank. My roommate (F. Thom) and I spent two years in this house and were sorry to have to move into the main residence." Doris (Wagar) Yuskin, Class of '45, had similar feelings, "When it came time to leave the stone house and move into the luxury of the nurses' home, I was sad. The old house had been a challenge to us. We met it head on and won. I regard my stay at it as one of the happiest years of my life."

During the summer of 1945, the main Nurses' Residence had a facelift to accommodate increasing staff and student needs. More rooms for the students were added to the upper floors, and staff quarters were all moved to the first floor. A new kitchenette and recreation room were added to the basement, and the living rooms were remodeled. Alberta Dow, Class of '37, reflected in the 1946 yearbook that "All in all, we have to admit that we have a very lovely home now – and I do know that a good many of us are thinking that we have probably trained a few years too soon."

1972 A.M.H. YEARBOOK

"The Stone House",
a temporary home for student nurses

Of the graduate nurses from the 1940's, two would go on to nurse in Central America. Violet Stelter, Class of '43, went to Nicaragua as a missionary with her husband, Reverend John Befus. Violet's training was invaluable in her work, as a public health instructor and life skills teacher. Agnes O'Neil, Class of '42, went to Golfito, Costa Rica, to work at the Golfito Hospital from 1948 to 1953.

1948 L.P.H. YEARBOOK

Nurses' Residence, with 1945 additions

1972 A.M.H. YEARBOOK

Lamont Clinic, 1947
Back left: Dr. J.A. Alton, Dr. A.E. Archer, Dr. J.B. Ringwood. Front left: Dr. M.A.R. Young, Dr. L. Weatherilt, Dr. W.R. Bell

There were several more changes in staff once the war was over. When Miss Sandell was able to return to Korea in 1945, Miss Helen Mayers came to work at Lamont as the Superintendent of Nurses. She was there until 1947, when she was succeeded by Mrs. Mary (Tokaruk) Cooper, (Class of '43) as Acting Superintendent of Nurses. There were three new doctors affiliated with the clinic in 1947: Dr. J.B. Ringwood, Dr. J.L. Weatherilt, and Dr. W.R. Bell, each of whom provided new skills. Dr. M.A.R. Young was appointed Acting Superintendent of Lamont Public Hospital in 1942.

1946 A.M.H. YEARBOOK

Miss Helen Mayers,
Superintendent of Nurses, 1945-47

Legislation regarding fire regulations was passed in Alberta making it unlawful to house patients on any floor above the second, in a frame building. Portions of the old wing were three levels and this meant this space was no longer useable. Permission was obtained to carry on until after the war years, when extensive discussions were carried on to resolve the problems. If the old wing had to be closed, there would be no way of meeting the demands for service, and the reduction in beds would mean the nurses' training program would have to close. After much careful consideration, in conjunction with the Home Mission Board, it was decided that new construction would be undertaken.

1972 A.M.H. YEARBOOK

Mrs. Mary Cooper,
Acting Superintendent of Nurses,
1947-1948

LPH/AMH ALUMNAE COLLECTION

Opening Ceremonies, 1948 wing

The estimated cost of the new wing, to increase bed capacity to 100 beds, was $180,000. The actual cost rose to $245,000. Raising funds for the project was a priority, and in addition to support from the Board of Home Missions and a government grant, a fund-seeking brochure was created to appeal to the whole Alberta Conference of the United Church for contributions to the new "Memorial Wing". The brochure contained the history of the hospital in words and pictures, and gave information about the current services of the hospital. Admissions in 1946 were 2558 with 9872 out-patients. Births had climbed to 189, and operations to 568. The average number of employees was 67, at a payroll cost of $3,726.70 per month. The total cost of operation for the year was $97,415.27.

Dr. Helen Houston, a medical missionary, first came to Lamont in 1948, in her 'pre-med' days as a summer relief cook. She returned as a medical student during a summer period before beginning her missionary work in India, and later Nepal. Lamont has been fortunate to see her several times since then, on her furloughs.

Things had certainly changed since the early days of the hospital. Infant mortality in the district fell from over 124 per 1000 in 1912 to 36 per 1000 in 1945. There had also been no maternal deaths in hospital in the last 1650 cases. In 1946, there were a surprising 449 patients seen at Lamont who had come from outside the Province.

At the opening ceremonies of the new wing, held in September, 1948, a newspaper reported that "patients from such points in Alberta as the City of Edmonton, towns of Wetaskiwin, Ponoka, Breton, Marwayne and Beauvallon were in the hospital while the ceremony was in progress. Patients from four Saskatchewan centres were also receiving treatment..." Lamont's reputation continued to grow beyond the confines of its own community.

1948 addition

1972 A.M.H. YEARBOOK

The opening ceremonies included dignitaries such as Dr. M.R. Bow, Alberta Deputy Minister of Health, who brought greetings from the government. Rev. Wesley Brainbridge, representing the Alberta Conference of the United Church, accepted custody of the new wing from Dr. Jones, past moderator of the United Church, and turned it over to the local board. Dr. Archer accepted on behalf of the board. Rev. Father H.G. Adams extended greetings from the Ukrainian Church, and remarked that the entire community and district appreciated the fine work of the hospital and its staff.

1972 A.M.H. YEARBOOK

Miss L. Marie Young,
Superintendent of Nurses, 1948-1963

And then arrived our new Matron, Miss Young, 100 pounds of revolutionary ideas! Altho' her drastic changes were, at first, not always accepted with approval, we all realize now, how much we have benefited by them. We shall not forget either, how she has won herself into our hearts.

– 1950 yearbook

One final note from the opening ceremony records tells us that "Members of the Hospital Aid provided coffee, tea and sandwiches for the visitors." This organization faithfully supported the work of the hospital, from its early beginnings in 1912 as the Lamont Public Hospital Aid Society, through its next name change to the Lamont Public Hospital Women's Auxiliary. Its quiet, yet steady support to patients, training school and staff has not gone unnoticed.

Mrs. Cooper was Acting Superintendent of Nurses until 1948, when Miss Marie Young arrived. She was a graduate of the Children's Hospital in Winnipeg, and later Toronto University. Miss Young contributed greatly to a "New Look" to the training school, that began when the 1948 wing freed up the third floor in the frame building, making new space available for classrooms and accommodations for junior students. New regulations governing the Schools of Nursing in the Province of Alberta, issued by the Senate of the University of Alberta in 1947, necessitated changes in the training school program as well.

This time of change seems also to have been reflected in the doctors, as two new doctors became affiliated with the Lamont clinic in 1948. Dr. A. Dobson had been at the George McDougall Hospital at Smoky Lake for several years prior to his arrival at Lamont, and was a member of the Alberta Conference Hospitals Board that oversaw the Lamont and Smoky Lake Hospitals. Dr. L.M. Davey also arrived around the same time.

Dr. L.M. Davey, arrived 1948

1950 A.M.H. YEARBOOK

Dr. A. Dobson, arrived 1948

In the midst of such growth and change as Lamont Public hospital was experiencing, Dr. Archer suffered his first coronary attack in January, 1949. Rather than succumb to the life of a semi-invalid, his decision was to continue to apply his energies to his chosen field, and he recovered enough to attend a hospital board meeting May 10, 1949. However, he experienced another coronary thrombosis on May 21, 1949, and entered the hospital at Lamont that same day. On May 23, 1949, Dr. Archer passed away peacefully in the hospital, where he had never before been a patient. He was seventy years old. Funeral services were held in the Lamont United Church, with interment at the Edmonton Cemetery. His wife, Jessie Valens Archer, lived another three years after his death before passing away from a malignant tumor.

LPH/AMH ALUMNAE COLLECTION

A painting of Dr. Archer by Andrew Anderson

Tributes to Dr. Archer came from his colleagues, fellow medical professional people, staff, students and community. Dr. M.A.R. Young was to say that "Albert Ernest Archer died as he had lived, with equanimity, unperturbed by the lesser affairs of men. He had an abiding faith in the Master of the Universe, and a charitable attitude toward the weaknesses of his fellow men. He felt honored in being a member of the Medical Profession and during his life time did much to maintain the dignity and prestige of the profession he loved so much."

The 1950 yearbook reads, "What should one say to be recorded in these pages as an epitaph? Those who knew him have their own thoughts and memories. To those who read these lines, not having known Dr. Archer, I can only say 'He was the Nurse's Friend.' He demonstrated this in his welcome to each new class, in his concern for the welfare of the Student Nurse, in his confidence that each Graduate would be a worthy member of her profession."

The community also remembered the loyal doctor who spent so many years of his life tending the needs of the pioneers. Eugenia Figol Symborski says, "We also remember our most beloved Dr. Archer, who was the kindest, most humble, and dedicated doctor to his patients and his profession. No matter how severe the weather, he was always willing to visit the sick. He, too, would stop over for a rest, a visit and a hot cup of tea, sometimes bringing his assistant Dr. Rush."

The passing of our great "Chief" Dr. Archer this year was keenly felt. His memory lingers with us. The L.P.H. of today stands as a living and tangible monument to his memory. We are deeply indebted to him and to his associates who have given so freely of their time and skill to this great cause to which they have dedicated their lives.

– Evelyn (McRoberts) Moore, Class of '44

LPH/AMH ALUMNAE COLLECTION

Stained glass window in Pediatrics ward, dedicated "In memory of Dr. A.E. Archer, a beloved physician"

Dr. Roy Anderson also paid Dr. Archer a great tribute in this story. In 1916, Dr. Archer drove out in his car late one night to bring Roy back to the hospital for treatment for peritonitis. Although Roy had only his Grade 8 education, he enjoyed many visits with Dr. Archer during his stay at the hospital. Dr. Archer encouraged Roy to consider going back to school, "so a few months later, while riding a bobsleigh on a beautiful winter's day, I decided to study medicine. At least six young people from the Lamont area went into medicine, inspired by Dr. Archer and his associates. And I believe that his excellent medical competence and his abiding Christian faith were the motivating forces."

A stained glass window was unveiled in the Children's Ward in September, 1950, in memory of Dr. Archer. It shows Jesus blessing the children and was created by Smitts and Ramsdale of Toronto. Supported by the many friends of Dr. Archer, the window became a symbol of many people's deep feelings for this "beloved physician".

A further tribute to Dr. Archer came with the re-naming of the hospital after September 24, 1950, to the "Archer Memorial Hospital". The "soul of this hospital" and the spirit of this man would continue to be woven together in the future, just as they had been through the past 37 years.

1951 A.M.H. YEARBOOK

Archer Memorial Hospital, 1951

CHAPTER 6
1950 TO 1959

RENEWING COMMITMENT

The death of Dr. Archer and change in the hospital's name marked a major turning point in the history of the Lamont Hospital. The work of the hospital as it had been envisioned was in new hands, and the Archer Memorial Hospital moved on to its new identity, while still retaining many original characteristics that had made it special. Even in its physical appearance, the hospital was a mix of old and new. The original frame building to the west received a face lift and underwent renovations to bring it into line with the new wing added in 1948. A new front entrance was added as well. The hospital boasted new efficiencies and a new look, yet retained the same original sense of purpose and commitment to high standards.

THE LAMP IS GOLDEN

Dr. M.A.R. Young, Superintendent, 1949-1978

One of Dr. Young's primary interests was in the Nurses' Training School and he had high expectations for the young women who came to a church hospital for their training. He firmly believed that each individual had potential far beyond their expectations and his method of teaching often contained the challenge to climb to greater heights of accomplishment. His demeanor was forceful at times, but always reflected the deepest integrity and the most noble of aspirations.

– Kent Harrold

As Dr. M.A.R. Young was to say in 1951, "Those of us who carry on at Archer Memorial Hospital do so with satisfaction and the hope that traditions are being maintained and new and better ones being established. That at least is the spirit of the Founder."

The Board of Home Missions of the United Church of Canada, still a major player at Lamont, appointed Dr. M.A.R. Young as Medical Superintendent of the hospital in 1949. As Acting Superintendent since 1942, he was the natural choice as Dr. Archer's successor. Dr. Young had the same sense of the importance of the hospital to the community, a deep commitment to the nurses' training program and an unfailing faith in the Christian perspective.

Like Dr. Archer, Dr. Young was a well known figure in the larger medical profession. He served as President of the Alberta Council of the College of Physicians and Surgeons for the 1947, 1948, and 1949 terms, and became President of the Alberta Division of the Canadian Medical Association for the 1956-1957 year.

The nurses who came to Lamont were also always encouraged to be the best. The presentation of awards for accomplishments was a tradition that had been started early in the training school's life, and in the 1950's there was a renewed interest in rewarding professionalism and fine nursing. The Canadian Nurse Award, in the form of a two year subscription to *The Canadian Nurse*, was first given in 1951 to Hazel Berg as recognition of "the graduate who has shown the greatest promise of professional development in their period of training." (Later this award was changed to recognize the student "who receives the highest standing in theory and practice in the first year of nursing," and was given to Katherine Bott, Class of '58.) A medal and cash award was also instituted

LPH/AMH ALUMNAE COLLECTION

Doreen Mitchell presents the Obstetrical Award to Annabelle Page, Class of '54 by Miss Doreen Mitchell, Class of '49, "in hopes of interesting students in Advanced Obstetrics." This award was first given to Marion Ashley, Class of '52. Pauline Bell, Class of '52, was the first recipient of "The Highest Standing in Nutrition" award.

During the 1950's, nurses in training were given new opportunities to expand their knowledge and experience through the addition of affiliations to their program, the process by which the nurses were able to learn specific specialties at other medical centres. "The word *affiliation* comes to us from the Latin", Dr. Young explained, "and means 'to adopt as a son'. Such affiliations should increase your knowledge, broaden your sympathies, and make you better nurses."

Initially, a one-day trip to the Oliver Institute in Edmonton was offered, to provide exposure to other types of cases and their treatment.The first formal affiliations were with the Mental Hospital at Ponoka (1950), and the Central Alberta Sanatorium in Calgary (1951). Two months duration was the norm at first, but it changed over time to four and six week affiliations. In 1955, the Pediatrics Ward of the University of Alberta Hospital added a pediatrics component. Time spent in the Lamont Clinic and the Lamont Health Region was also classed as an affiliation.

The Provincial Mental Hospital for many of us has become a part of our work where we gained much new experience in just two short months. We went, feeling much like "probies", in our new work, but returned having had a glimpse into the importance of psychiatric nursing and the part it plays in the world today.

– 1951 yearbook

1951 A.M.H. YEARBOOK

Main Building, Provincial Mental Hospital, Ponoka, Alberta, one of Archer Memorial's affiliated hospitals

In 1954, the Young People's Union of the United Church entered and won the provincial drama festival. Three students of Archer Memorial Hospital School of Nursing and a former student assisted. Ruth-Marie Kreiger, Shirley (Leitch) Harrold and her husband Kent, Louise Kleparchuk, Edna Dodds, and other student members who provided technical support, put on "Sunday Cost Five Pesos" under the direction of Margaret Nix. Ruth-Marie Kreiger earned the "best supporting actress" award, and Margaret Nix won the trophy for "best director".

Another program started during this time was that of Civil Defense. Since the war, the protection of communities had become an area of concern. The first course in Civil Defense was offered in 1951, to Directors of Nursing, Matrons and other nursing professionals. Miss L.M. Young (Director of Nursing), Miss Connick (Public Health Unit nurse), and Mrs. Florence Love (Alumnae, Class of '22) attended a four-day course given at the University of Alberta. A requirement of these participants was that they would offer two days of lectures to the nurses in their own districts. Subsequently, a class was organized for 1952, which 35 nurses attended, and a second class was offered the following year.

On August 26, 1953, a group of medical and nursing staff and Alumnae gathered to hear the first lecture in a series initiated by Mrs. Margaret (Archer) Buchanan, daughter of Dr. Archer. She felt that it would provide both a memorial to her father, and a special event for the students. Believed to be the first lectureship of its kind offered to a School of Nursing in Canada, it drew a great deal of interest. The first lecture was given by Miss Helen Penhale, Professor of Nursing, University of Alberta, on the topic of "The International Congress of Nurses" held in Brazil, during the summer of 1953. The lectures were later held in the Lamont United Church from 1954, with the public invited to attend. Dr. E.P. Scarlett, Chancellor of the University of Alberta, gave the 1954 lecture on "The Ages of Man". The lectureship continued for many years of the training program, featuring such distinguished speakers as Dr. T.C. Routby, President of the Canadian Medical and British Medical Associations; Dean D.J.C. Elson, St. Stephen's College; and Dr. Elmer E. Roper, Mayor of Edmonton.

LPH/AMH ALUMNAE COLLECTION

Stained glass window in Lamont United Church, 1954, dedicated to Dr. A.E. Archer's memory

On June 6, 1954, a Dedication Service was held for the stained glass window to Dr. Archer's memory in the Lamont United Church. The Alumnae classes up to and including 1950 contributed to the window. The centre panel was placed especially for Dr. Archer, with other panels in memory of Mrs. Archer, Mr. S. Anderson and Mr. G. Christie. Dr. Young wrote in a tribute for the occasion, "To those of us who knew him we have our own memorials, to strangers and even to those yet unborn some tangible mark must be left to note that a great man has passed this way... It is a fitting and beautiful tribute to a kind friend and teacher...."

Although the Hospital Board's presence is usually in the background, it contributes greatly to the smooth operation of a hospital. The hospital at Lamont grew from its earliest stages, guided by a body known as the Alberta Conference Hospitals Board, which oversaw the running of the hospitals at both Lamont and Smoky Lake. In May, 1939, a new face appeared on the board, Nelles V. Buchanan, from Edmonton. His father, Rev. T.C. Buchanan, had been deeply involved in the early development of Lamont Public Hospital through his position with the Methodist Church Home Missions. Nelles Buchanan became the Chairman of the Board on August 25, 1944. In 1953, the custom was started of having the Chairman of the Board bring greetings to the graduating nurses within the pages of the yearbook, and the profile of the Board and its involvement became more visible.

1956 A.M.H. YEARBOOK

Chief Judge Nelles V. Buchanan, Chairman of the Hospital Board

Because of increasing complexity and administrative requirements, more effective business management was required. On May 10, 1949, the Board appointed Mr. John Matwichuk as Acting Business Manager of the Hospital. Later in 1953, Mr. N.F. Mutter of Kingston, Ontario, was approached by the Board to consider the position of a hospital administrator, a position which he accepted.

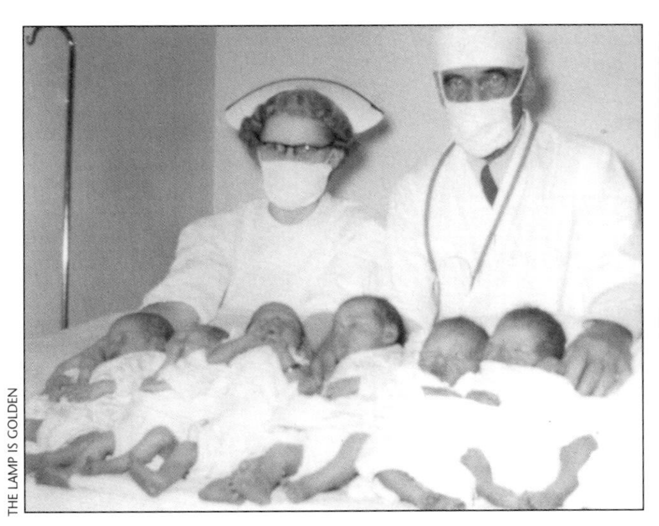

THE LAMP IS GOLDEN

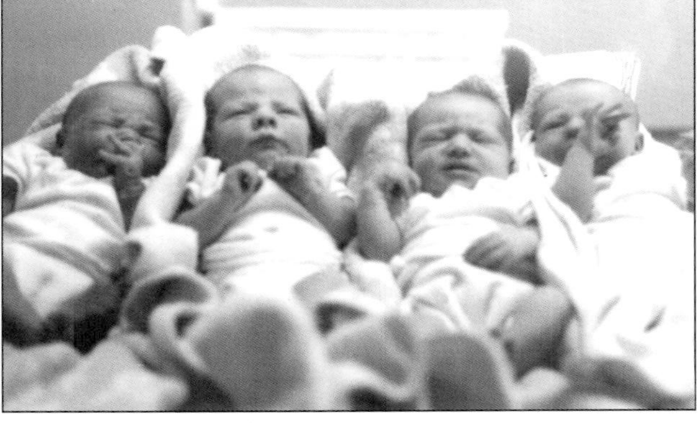

THE LAMP IS GOLDEN

Changes in the Maternity Wing

With most mothers now giving birth to their children in the hospital, home deliveries were a thing of the past. The "Mat Bag" was dismantled for good on September 21, 1953

Dr. Alton and his staff were kept busy with three sets of twins and a set of quadruplets born at the hospital

Left: Twins – children of Mrs. Leo Tkachuk, Mrs. Audrey Rinas, and Mrs. Ted Osbaldeston

Right: Quadruplets born in the 1950's. Names not available

We are happy to report that in spite of several years of very little publicity, the ancient society of I Eta Pie is still flourishing and thriving on whatever is available. Such things as cookies from home are most popular, but almost anything edible is made use of and don't we show it!

– 1954 yearbook

Miss Florence Courtice,
Associate Director of Nursing, 1955

Miss N.E. Davidson,
Instructress, 1952-1962

Miss Audrey Wright,
Hospital Visitor, 1954-1958

Other new faces arrived at Lamont, to take up a variety of roles and responsibilities at the Archer Memorial Hospital. Miss Florence Courtice came on staff as Associate Director of Nursing Service, in August, 1955, replacing Mrs. Donna Weatherilt who had been serving in that capacity. Miss Norah E. Davidson assumed the responsibility for classroom instruction in 1952, and continued in the role of Associate Director of Nursing Education until 1962.

When Rev. C.W.W. Ross moved to Smoky Lake in 1936, the role of the hospital chaplain was taken over by the resident minister of the United Church at Lamont. However, it became increasingly obvious that there was a great need for a permanent or resident chaplain. In the summer of 1954, Miss Audrey Wright arrived to carry out this work under the title "Hospital Visitor". From Kitchener, Ontario, Miss Wright studied at Emmanuel Bible College in Kitchener, then worked for two years as a field secretary for Waterloo County W.C.T.U. Her work at Archer Memorial Hospital, where she represented the United Church of Canada and worked closely with the local United Church, included caring for the spiritual needs of patients, staff and students.

Among the student nurses, too, there were new faces. Kay Hong and Sung Soon Yew came from Korea to take training programs at the Archer Memorial Hospital. They were sponsored by the Women's Missionary Society, through their association with Ada Sandell at a hospital in Korea.

One of the student nurses' events that was continued throughout the 1950's was the Capping Ceremony. This was begun during the time of Miss Ada Sandell in the 1940's, to mark the transition between being a "probie" (probationer) and becoming a full-fledged nursing student. It became a solemn occasion for the student nurses, one which they were unwilling to discontinue despite several suggestions to that effect. Another of their special rituals involved the moving of the black bands on the caps, to signify the different stages of training between intermediates and seniors. At graduation, the points of the cap were spread as well, which ultimately gave rise to the new name for the yearbook that was adopted in 1957 – "Wings and Bands".

It's only a piece of cotton.
Starched stiff and scrupulously clean.
Folded and pinned, crudely at first,
But worn with a radiant gleam.

It's only a band of black velvet
That marks you – a Second Year;
But it means you have made an
advancement
Along a tough road – your career.

It's only a cap with the velvet,
Moved to the tip of the wings;
But it means you have come a long way,
Have seen and learned many things.

Yes – it's only a starched piece of cotton,
Folded and pinned at the seams;
But there are no words in the language
That can say what your cap means.

– Margaret (Hemphill) Hougan,
Class of '54

1952 A.M.H. YEARBOOK

Christmas Melodies – a chance for musical talents to shine

The student nurses during this time were busy not only with their formal studies, but also additional opportunities for self-development. A number of student nurses were able to attend conventions of their professional organizations. In 1950, several students attended the Alberta Association of Registered Nurses sessions in Edmonton, and the Canadian Nurses Association conference held in various cities across Canada from 1950 onward. Others were busy preparing a yearbook for each year, or involved in fund raising events to help defray the cost of the books (such as the 1954 yearbook of 64 pages which cost $565.18). Participating in bible study with Dr. Young's group, or sharing their musical talents with the community through the "Christmas Melodies" presentation allowed many students other avenues for developing their skills and talents.

The Student Nurses' Association, under the sponsorship of the Alberta Association of Registered Nurses, came into being at the A.A.R.N. convention, 1954. Its members would come from the 12 training schools across Alberta, including Lamont which always sent a representative to the S.N.A.A. In 1957-1958, Viola Maggs, Class of '58, was elected the Provincial President of S.N.A.A.

The 1956 yearbook tells of the passing of one who was a friend to many of the graduates of the hospital. Mrs. R.E. Harrison (Christine Musselman) died on December 10, 1956. Her two years as Matron of Lamont Public Hospital (1917-1919), her marriage to Lamont druggist R. E. Harrison, and her many years of service to the Women's Missionary Society reflected her on-going commitment to her adopted community of Lamont. It was also noted in 1956 that Mr. R.E. Harrison, who had been a member the first Hospital Board, had only missed four graduations in 41 years. He passed away in the spring of 1958.

Marie Lechuk, Class of '55, had an article on "Neurofibroma of Spinal Cord" published as a Student Care Study Issue in the September, 1956 issue of Davis' Nursing Survey *and in* The Canadian Nurse, *February, 1957. Irene Prochnau, Class of '53, spent time nursing in Nicaragua. Herta Richter, Class of '55, served at Fort Good Hope, N.W.T., as a nurse at the Indian and Northern Health Services nursing station.*

LPH/AMH ALUMNAE COLLECTION

Field trip to Civil Defense headquarters, Class of 1958

After the Civil Defense courses offered in the early 1950's, the Alberta Emergency Measures Organization became the principle trainer for Civil Defense, and all hospitals were encouraged to develop plans for safe and efficient evacuation and admittance of patients in emergency situations. The first test of the Archer Memorial Hospital's procedures was held on May 15, 1957. All departments were on alert, as 45 simulated casualties from a "disaster at the nickel plant at Fort Saskatchewan" arrived, while Civil Defense and EMO officials observed the procedures. Members of the Hospital Women's Auxiliary, the Legion, the R.C.A.F. Air Cadets, the C.G.I.T. and high school students participated in varying roles. It was an exercise that was repeated the following year, and was put to a true test later in 1960 with the major bus-train accident in Lamont.

Miss Davidson is my teacher,
I shall not pass.
She leadeth me to the chalk
For my bloc's sake.
Yea, though I walk through the
valley of the shadow of knowledge
I learn not: for I am dumb.
My anatomy text and my pen
they accompany me.
She maketh me to show my ignorance
before my fellow students,
She annointeth my head with
Nursing Arts.
Surely drug problems shall follow me
all the days of my life
And I shall dwell in the
probie bloc forever.

– Anonymous, 1958 Yearbook

Pulling together was a common occurrence at Lamont. Valedictorian Donna Carlyle, Class of 1957, stated, "We feel our class is closer than friends, closer than classmates because we [have] not only worked, lived, studied and played together, but more important[ly], grown up together. This has made us more like sisters. If it had not been for one another, we probably would not have made the grade. I know we will never, never forget how we stood by each other." This was no doubt true for many of the classes, as well as the staff.

Medical staff as of July, 1957 included Dr. M.A.R. Young (Superintendent), Dr. J. Alton, Dr. J.L. Weatherilt, Dr. T.A. Dobson, and Dr. D.R. Young. The Training School Staff was still headed by Miss L. Marie Young (Director of Nursing), Miss F. Courtice (Assistant Director of Nursing), Miss N. Davidson and Miss N. Dick as Instructresses, and Miss V. Alho as Operating Room Supervisor. Mr. John Matwichuk continued to provide administrative support.

1972 A.M.H. YEARBOOK

Class of 1957: two gold medals were awarded that year because of a tie in marks. Recipients were Donna Carlyle and Joan King

With the installation of a new 300 am. X-ray unit in 1954, and the addition of a small unit for taking chest x-rays of all admissions, the Radiology department was updated to more modern standards. Later, Dr. Z. Gutter became the consulting radiologist around 1958, and was a familiar face for many years at the Archer.

Dr. Lloyd Davey left Lamont for Toronto in 1957 with his family, to take up work more suited to him since he had contracted poliomyelitis in 1952. He, like so many of the doctors, had been an active community member, serving on a committee that built a new United Church manse, after a fire in August, 1950, completely destroyed the original building.

ALONG VICTORIA TRAIL

Dr. Davey and associates

Top row, left to right:
Dr. Chai, Dr. R. Young,
Dr. Albert Dobson, Dr. Lloyd Weatherilt

Bottom row, left to right:
Dr. Lloyd Davey, Dr. Jack Alton,
Dr. Morley A.R. Young

Dr. Jack Alton, retired in February, 1958, due to ill health. His daughter, Nancy (Alton) McMurchy, reflecting on his career at Lamont, said, "His special interest in medicine was obstetrics and he must have delivered enough babies, during his 35 years there, to populate a small town!"

During Dr. Young's term as President of the Alberta Division of the Canadian Medical Association, he was named as President-Elect of the Canadian Medical Association for the 1957-1958 term. The 1957 yearbook committee paid this tribute to Dr. Young, "To those of us who have come to know and appreciate Dr. Young in the classroom, in the operating room, on the ward, or in the church and community, it is good to know his influence is also recognized and appreciated all across Canada." It is of interest that both Dr. Archer and Dr. Young attained this prestigious and responsible position in their respective careers. It says a great deal about the calibre of the medical professionals who had chosen to serve in the little town of Lamont, Alberta.

Closer to home, discussions were begun in the fall of 1957 regarding the construction of a new nurses' residence. The plans included seventy beds for accommodation, suitable provisions for the training program, and an auditorium for social functions. Plans were finalized in late 1958 and construction begun in January, 1959. During this phase of construction, a service building was also built to the north of the hospital, containing a carpenter's shop, a paint shop, a garage for the truck, a pipe storage area and a storage room for records.

Dr. Alton dearly loved the outdoors and spent many happy hours with his dogs hunting and hiking in the woods. He and the family for many years spent their summers at their cottage at Elk Island Park, where the Archers, the Youngs, the Shears, the Adams, the Hansons, and the Harrisons also had summer cottages.

– Nancy (Alton) McMurchy

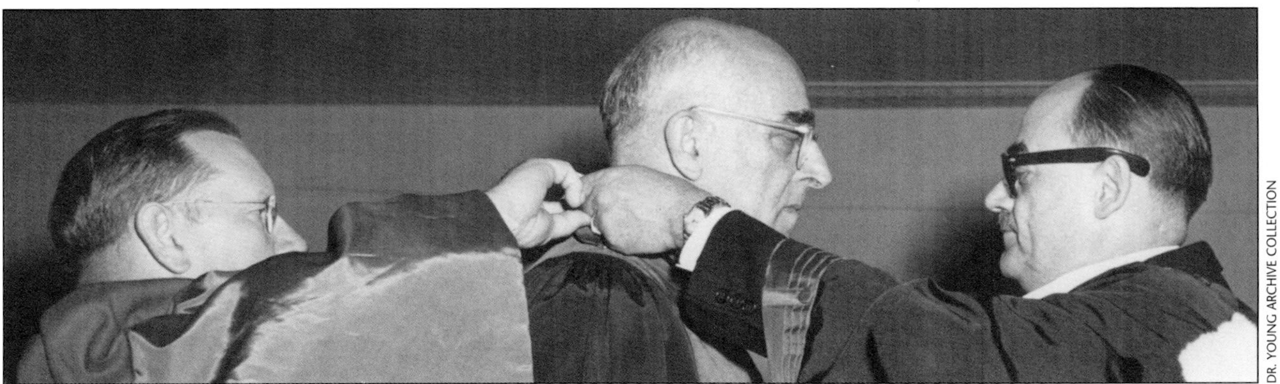

DR. YOUNG ARCHIVE COLLECTION

Dr. Young receives his chain of office as CMA President, from Renaud Lemieux (right) and Norman Gosse (left)

1960 A.M.H. YEARBOOK

Miss Kathryn Hurlburt,
Hospital Chaplaincy Program

In 1958, Miss Audrey Wright moved on to other work and studies. Her work was taken up by Miss Kathryn Hurlburt during the summer of 1959, when she was a Theological Student at St. Stephen's College, Edmonton. Once she had achieved her ordination, Miss Hurlburt took a course for hospital chaplains at the Massachusetts General Hospital. She returned to Lamont to set up a complete hospital chaplaincy service at the Archer Memorial Hospital. Her tasks included lectures to the students on curricular subjects as well as on meeting the spiritual needs of patients. She was also a counselor to many who needed her help, and held Bible study groups for the students.

The role of the United Church in church-sponsored hospitals went through an examination during the later 1950's. Archer Memorial Hospital was one of several hospitals that was carefully assessed by the United Church with regard to the role of the Church in its future. It was decided that United Church involvement was still an important component for the Archer Memorial, and that building the future on a solid past was a goal to be continued.

1954 A.M.H. YEARBOOK

Rastus, friend to all. A very important member of student extra curricular activities was "Rastus". Wherever students tried to have a picnic, a bonfire or just a walk downtown by one, two or more, Rastus was in their midst, on all fours, tail wagging, a grin on his face, and tongue hanging out from extra exertion. Rastus was the big, black Newfoundland member of the M.A.R. Young family. He never told how he knew nurses from ordinary folk.

– L. Marie Young

Dr. Young was the speaker at the Archer Memorial Lecture in October, 1958. He brought his considerable talents as a historian and writer to the occasion as he remembered his long association with Dr. Archer, renewing a sense of Dr. Archer both as professional colleague and personal friend. He then went on to talk about his experiences travelling across Canada as the Canadian Medical Association President, and brought the future into focus for the listeners. What he did in this lecture, he had been doing at Lamont all along – reflecting on the past and integrating it into the present, then looking from the present to a bright future.

With Dr. Young's guidance, and with the renewed commitment of all involved, the Archer Memorial Hospital made the transition through the 1950's to a new name and sense of identity coupled with the old ideals and standards of excellence that had always been a part of its history.

LPH/AMH ALUMNAE COLLECTION

Nurses' Residence under construction

CHAPTER 7
1960 TO 1969

MILESTONES AND TURNING POINTS

The architect's plans were prepared, the contractor was hired and the financing put in place. Everyone was excited to see the project go ahead. After 43 years of various accommodation arrangements for student nurses, the dream of a new Nurses' Residence was finally beginning to take shape. The planning stages had considered not only the accommodation needs of the student nurses, but also the need to provide adequate teaching facilities for students and staff.

Contributions to the new residence included a donation from the Provincial Women's Association of the United Church towards the provision of linen for the new facility. The Alumnae Association, in conjunction with the Women's Auxiliary of the hospital, furnished a room in the residence which was dedicated on June 5th, 1960. This ceremony granted tenure of the room to the Alumnae Association, for its use in furthering the "purposes for which the Alumnae was organized."

For Dr. Morley A.R. Young and many other staff, it was "A Dream Come True". In his address at the opening ceremonies of the residence, Dr. Young said, "This building serves a threefold purpose. It is a home for our Nurses, Graduates and those in Training. It provides recreational facilities in an effort to overcome Prince Phillip's criticism of our weaknesses. The third and most important purpose is that this is a School for Nursing. Education is being stressed more and more in the training of a nurse and provision has been made here for that activity." In addition to its 71 bed accommodation and teaching facilities, there was also a laboratory/demonstration area, staff offices, linen and laundry rooms, trunk storage areas, a matron's suite, and a lounge area for social events.

Of the total cost of $347,000, over $142,000 were government grants. The remaining $205,000 was underwritten by the Board of Home Missions of the United Church of Canada, to be refunded over a twenty year period by the Provincial Government. Dr. M.C. Macdonald, Secretary of the Board of Home Missions, was in attendance at the opening ceremonies and paid tribute to the "determination and realism" shown by Dr. Young and Chief Judge Buchanan, as well as to the support of the provincial and federal governments in this project.

LPH/AMH ALUMNAE COLLECTION

The new Nurses' Residence and teaching facility opened February 8, 1960

Above: Classroom area of the new teaching facilities

Below: Student's room in the new residence

1960 A.M.H. YEARBOOK

The year 1960 was also noted for several other events. The old Nurses' Home was now vacant, except for the memories of the many nurses who had lived there during their three years of training. In April, 1960, the building was slowly dismantled and hauled away.

Dr. M.C. Macdonald of the Board of Home Missions returned to Lamont later that same year to act as Chairman of a "Doctors' Conference" held in September, 1960. Doctors from hospitals operating under the auspices of the United Church of Canada attended. At this conference it was decided that the United Church of Canada would establish a bursary to assist young women wishing to enter nursing.

Dr. Young wrote about the 1960 opening of a physiotherapy department in the Archer Memorial Hospital, serving both old and young, that "The problem of keeping people active increases daily and this department is doing a very good job in that field. We wonder how we got along without it for so many years."

An event on November 29, 1960, that would leave its mark on Lamont forever is related in a first-person narrative in the Alumnae archives by a staff member of Archer Memorial Hospital. "The Associate Director of Nursing and the Health Nurse were both off. For this reason I was in the Nursing Service Office preparing for ward rounds shortly before 9 a.m. The telephone rang. It was the station agent who stated that he had just witnessed the train strike a school bus. Would I please send trucks and doctors."

A west-bound train had struck a loaded school bus at a level crossing on the east side of the Town of Lamont. The staff at the hospital responded to the emergency. "Here is where the Civil Defense courses, exercises and yearly review of paper work with each class of students proved of value. The staffs and students immediately started preparing beds, and setting up the minimum paper work. Some from the O.R. took supplies to all wards and set intravenous equipment into each room."

Casualties started to arrive. "I was on the elevator, and there stayed until all casualties were in beds. Probably not more than ten minutes had passed since the first telephone call." A Surgical Team from the Emergency Services Organization arrived about noon and "it was amazing to see how well these teams worked in strange surroundings." Offers of assistance poured in, and nursing services were augmented by 30 additional R.N.'s and 1 certified Nursing Aide in the first 24 hours. "Due to the physical plan of the hospital, with many single rooms, and the condition of the patients, many unconscious and semi-conscious, it was necessary to have a nurse with many patients 24 hours for some days." Over the period of November 29 to December 31, 1960, there were a total of 70 Registered Nurses over the regular staff, 2 nursing aides and 5 orderlies.

At the final count, there were 17 young people dead and 24 others injured, including the bus driver. A mass prayer and funeral service was held December 2 and 3, 1960, in Chipman for 14 of the victims. Services for the other three were held in Edmonton and Calmar.

At first we were stunned by the initial news and then we tried to help with the best of our ability. One of our biggest problems was that of emotional control – to remain calm when we saw bereaved and worried parents of seriously injured teenagers close to our own age, and to care for young people, some with whom we were acquainted.

After a long day, many of us felt exhausted from the strain of the day, but relieved because we felt we had done our best. Some of the Pre-Clinical Students, still unsure of nursing as a career, were then certain that they could become capable, helpful people and good nurses.

– 1960 yearbook

KIRK HARROLD

The plaque in Lamont Secondary School, honouring the bus-train accident victims of November 29, 1960

Dr. Young wrote of the accident later, "In the story of a hospital and its personnel it must be recorded that all acquitted themselves nobly and earned the gratitude of many and the praise of all. Time and effort did not count, many young people were suffering and help was gladly given. 'Well done Archer Memorial'."

The community was rocked to the core by the tragedy, and it will likely still be quite some time before memories of that cold November morning will be healed.

IN MEMORY OF
JOHN A. ALTON M.B.
FOR THIRTY-FOUR YEARS
OBSTETRICIAN IN THIS HOSPITAL
"A LIFE OF COMPASSION DEVOTED
TO THE SERVICE OF OTHERS"
THIS MEMORIAL AFFECTIONATELY PLACED
HERE BY THE ALUMNAE ASSOCIATION
OF THE ARCHER MEMORIAL HOSPITAL
OF LAMONT SCHOOL OF NURSING

1963 A.M.H. YEARBOOK

Plaque dedicated to Dr. J. Alton, physician at Lamont for 34 years

"When death draws down the curtain of the night,
And those we love in his deep darkness hides,
We can but wait the coming of the light,
And bless the memory that still abides."

...the memory that still abides... As true for the families of the bus-train accident as for the friends and family of Dr. John Alton, who passed away May 7, 1961. A tribute to Dr. Alton in the 1961 yearbook bears these words: "Among the hundreds of Graduates who wear a pin from Lamont, he had a host of friends. They regret the fact that he is not around any longer, but appreciate having had him as a friend and teacher." At a dedication service held on May 17, 1963, the Alumnae of the Lamont Public/Archer Memorial Hospital presented a plaque to be hung in the Obstetrical Department, a "memorial to a compassionate man whose life was service to his patients."

Changes in staff mean losses and gains. Miss Norah Davidson, who had given ten years service to the teaching faculty of the School of Nursing left Lamont to return to Manitoba. She was succeeded by Miss Lorna Churchill, as Associate Director of Nursing Education. Miss Margaret Brown replaced Miss Florence Courtice as Associate Director of Nursing Service. Other nursing school staff throughout the later 1960's, for shorter or longer periods, included Miss D. Barter, Mrs. Myrtle MacDonald, and Mr. G. Murphy (in the role of Associate Director of Nursing Education) Miss M. Middleton (Assistant, Nursing Office) and Mrs. Bernice Schneider (as Associate Director of Nursing Service). A talented group of instructresses added much to the theoretical part of the student nurse's training, as did the doctors of the Lamont Clinic who continued to offer their knowledge to the students. Stewart Harrison (a nephew of R.E. Harrison), who had been in charge of the dispensary at the hospital, was replaced by L. "Bud" Haverstock when Stewart sold his drug store in town. Dr. John Sunley, a graduate of Manitoba, became part of the medical staff in 1961. Dr. R. Young moved on to Fort Saskatchewan, and Dr. Dave Preston (from Bella Bella Hospital) and Dr. Ross Armstrong (from Hazelton Hospital) were part of the staff during the 1960's.

1963 A.M.H. YEARBOOK

Dr. John Sunley, photo taken 1962

As the 50th Anniversary of the hospital neared in 1962, preparations for a celebration began. Florence (MacDonald) Love, Class of '22, compiled a history of the hospital and the School of Nursing from its inception. "The Lamp is Golden", published in conjunction with the 50th Anniversary celebrations, provided a record in photos and text of the many people who had contributed to the hospital over the years.

AMH ARCHIVES

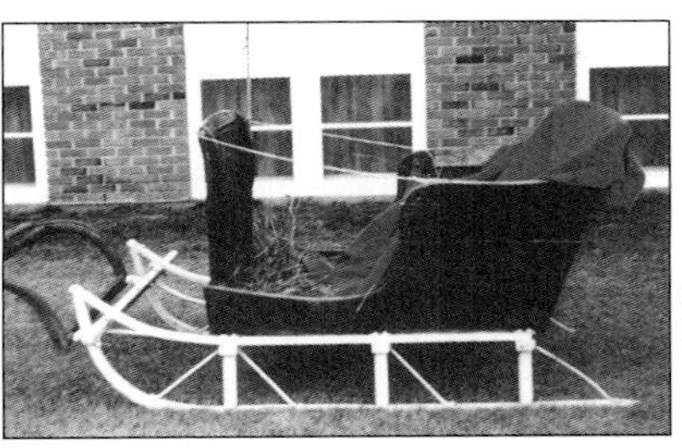

AMH ARCHIVES

Dr. Archer's summer and winter transportation, one of many historical exhibits at the 50th Anniversary celebrations

The celebrations began August 3, 1962, at 8:00 p.m. with a formal event to which many honored guests were invited. Included were a number of "firsts" for the hospital – the first patient, Charles Whittaker; the first graduate nurse, Mrs. W.E. Bluett (Purschke, Class of '15); and the first baby born in the hospital, Mrs. A. Leraand. Other dignitaries included His Honor J. Percy Page, Lieutenant Governor of Alberta; Rev. R. Douglas Smith of the United Church of Canada; and Alderman H.J. McKim Ross, who gave the 10th Annual Archer Memorial Lecture. Mr. Ross was originally from Lamont, and had known Dr. Archer well.

A tour to Elk Island National Park culminated in a wiener roast and picnic luncheon at noon on Saturday, August 4. A dinner was held Saturday evening at the nurses' residence, at which Miss E. Amaron, Secretary-Director of the Y.M.C.A. Edmonton was guest speaker. A special church service for nurses was held on Sunday, August 5 at 2:00 p.m., after various class reunions Sunday morning. Miss Ada Sandell was the guest speaker at the church service. Later Sunday, there was a farewell tea which was open to the public. Many graduates and their families attended the full weekend's events.

Dr. Young summed up the celebrations with these remarks, "Our wildest expectations were fulfilled and few, if any, had any criticism... History says it was a great event, adequately recognized and well managed... It was the sincere hope of all that the next fifty years would continue to be one of service and good work in the name of our church and of those who had pioneered this hospital effort."

The 50th Anniversary celebration was an opportunity to "view the 'new look' of the hospital and thrill over the comfort and convenience of the lovely new residence" and to "wonder that although some of our medical and nursing staff have been replaced, some changed physically, the all-over spirit that prevails is as we would wish to remember it."

– Barbara A. (Brown) Shearer, Class of '51

AMH ARCHIVES

Uniform Parade, part of the 50th Anniversary celebrations

1965 A.M.H. YEARBOOK

Miss Ethel C. James,
Director of Nursing, 1963-1972

In a tribute to Miss Young, the student nurses said, "Though we were apprehensive of your perfection, we all admired your efficiency and skill in organizing and administration of our hospital and school of nursing. Our new residence now standing remains as a tribute of your untiring efforts for us. Each of us will remember the significant events: Capping, Band Raising, White shoes and Stockings, Easter and Christmas Morning Services and Graduation, which through your careful plans and arrangements were made truly memorable occasions."

– 1964 yearbook staff

After all the excitement of anniversary celebrations, it was back to business as usual, but with a number of changes on the horizon. In June, 1962, an Order-in-Council was put in place by the Provincial Government to form the Lamont-Smoky Lake Auxiliary Hospital District #23, and discussions began regarding the development of an Auxiliary Hospital to ease the load of care at the active Archer Memorial.

In June, 1963, Miss Young announced her retirement from the position of Director of Nursing. After 15 years in this position, her presence would be missed by many. Miss Young was persuaded to stay on staff until October, 1963, when Miss Ethel James arrived to take up the challenge as Director of Nursing.

Miss Kathryn Hurlburt continued to provide a strong Chaplaincy program at the Archer Memorial Hospital. Under her able guidance, students from the Theology Program at St. Stephen's College in Edmonton came to AMH for lectures by Dr. Young and experience in hospital chaplaincy. Meetings were also held among the various clergy of denominations other than the United Church, who had members of their congregations in the hospital. Miss Hurlburt worked at the Archer Memorial until 1965, when she moved on to a new position as minister at Southminster United Church, Lethbridge, Alberta.

Dr. Young continued his active involvements with organizations on a national and international scale. He served as the Canadian Medical Association representative to the Medical Research Council, 1958-1961; Chairman of the Joint Committee of Nursing, 1958-1964; and Canadian delegate to the World Medical Association, 1959-1961. He received the Centennial Medal in 1967 and was made Officer of the Order of the Hospital of St. John of Jerusalem in 1969. He was made a Life member of the Alberta Medical Association in 1970.

1964 A.M.H. YEARBOOK

1964 A.M.H. YEARBOOK

Visits from medical students, nursing staff and doctors from overseas were quite common at the Archer Memorial Hospital. In the 1964 yearbook was the story of two "Korean Friends", Miss Kim and Miss Wee. Miss Kim graduated from Yonsei University and instructed at the National Medical Centre in Seoul before coming to Canada. Miss Wee graduated from the Presbyterian Medical Centre, Chunju Chulla pook-do, and worked at the Union Christian Hospital in Wonju. While at Lamont, both nurses were able to "observe new techniques in nursing care as well as improve their abilities in speaking, reading and writing the English language... they also offered much toward an understanding of their country, Korea."

By 1964, the Town of Lamont had put in place a water and sewage system which finally relieved many of the "water worries" that had plagued the hospital over the years. The "dam", which had served so well over many years, was finally drained later in May, 1967.

Lamont's hospital had always been known for its exceptional staff (it was, in its early days, referred to as "The Little Mayo"), and recognition from the larger medical community was ongoing. Judge Nelles V. Buchanan, Chairman of the Hospital Board, was awarded a Fellowship from the American College of Hospital Administrators in 1962, and the Canadian Hospital Association recognized his service to the Canadian hospital field with the George Findlay Stephens Award in May, 1965. In August, 1963, Dr. Young received the same Fellowship award from the American Association of Hospital Administrators, and was named a Senior Member of the Canadian Medical Association in 1966.

ALONG VICTORIA TRAIL

Lamont-Smoky Lake Auxiliary Hospital, opened in 1964

The doors to the new Auxiliary Hospital were opened on November 3, 1964, when the first patients took up residency in the hospital. The official opening of the unit took place on February 10, 1965, with the full occupancy of the unit reached by August 4, 1965 as the 8 private and 42 public beds were filled. Dr. Young, as administrator, oversaw the work force of 27 in nursing, dietary, laundry, housekeeping and clerical capacities, who provided for the care of the patients.

Over the next several years, Dr. Morley Young slowly decreased his practice and lectures for the nursing program, and increased his responsibilities as Administrator for the Auxiliary Hospital.

He made many presentations and wrote a great deal during this time. For example, "A Disaster Plan in a Small Hospital – As Seen in Theory and Reality", was presented to the Northern Regional Conference of the Associated Hospitals of Alberta, 1964; as President of the Alberta Council on Aging during 1967-1968, he presented an "Address to the Alberta Committee on Aging", 1966; and he spoke in church-related addresses, such as "The Pastor, the Physician and the Patient", 1966.

ALONG VICTORIA TRAIL

Mrs. Clara Course being welcomed by Dr. Young and Mrs. F. Neuman as the first patient in the new Auxiliary Hospital at Lamont

Outreach had always been an important part of the hospital at Lamont, and that practice continued in the 1960's. The Student Nurses' Association (S.N.A.) of Archer Memorial assisted the work of Miss Kay Hong, a 1954 graduate of Archer Memorial. Sending used textbooks for use in her nursing education program at Ewha Women's University, Seoul, Korea, contributed to her work. The Student Nurses' Association of Alberta (S.N.A.A.) also donated $250 (part proceeds from two talent shows) in support of her work in Korea.

Along with the construction of the Auxiliary Hospital, there was a major renovation to the Archer Memorial begun in February, 1965. The original 1912 wing, which had served over 50 years, was taken down piece by piece to make room for a new half-a-million dollar expansion. The new wing, built by Poole Construction Co. with Rule, Wynn, and Rule as architects, housed new laboratory and X-ray departments, operating rooms, chapel, cafeteria and physiotherapy facilities. The hospital beds were adjusted to 73, plus 10 bassinettes, with the Auxiliary Hospital taking over greater care of the elderly.

1965 A.M.H. YEARBOOK

Left: Old 1912 wing being demolished, to make way for the new wing construction, 1965

Below: New wing under construction

AMH ARCHIVES

1966 A.M.H. YEARBOOK

1972 A.M.H. YEARBOOK

Top: New 1965 wing, architect's rendering

Below: Chapel of the new wing

The official opening ceremonies of the new wing took place on May 12, 1966. A quote in the 1972 yearbook captures the feelings of the time: "Service to those in need is still our first consideration, we continue to operate under the auspices of the United Church, we continue to employ a loyal and dedicated staff, professional and lay, and we will continue to hope for the approval and friendship of the community."

1972 A.M.H. YEARBOOK

Class of 1965, the 50th class to graduate from this School of Nursing. Eight of the members of this class married young men of the Lamont area

We dressed Winnie Nelson, who was a senior student, in a kerchief and an old dress and padded her tummy with a pillow. She was bent over in the wheelchair, moaning and groaning, and we wheeled her to the second floor pretending she was a maternity patient in labour. The girls went scrambling and set up the Case Room and opened the maternity bundle, and never realized it was joke until they lifted her from the wheelchair onto the Case Room table.

– Muriel (Craig) Mitchell, Class of '60

The School of Nursing at the Archer Memorial Hospital was a continuing source of pride as its graduates spread out into communities all over Alberta to offer their nursing skills. The effect of the training school on the Lamont area itself was significant. Of the graduates from this School of Nursing, 109 married local young men. Eight out of a class of seventeen young women in the 1965 class, and seven out of a class of twenty in the 1966 class chose to call Lamont "home base".

Affiliations were still a part of the students' program throughout these years, although there were a few changes to that pattern. The Class of '60 began a psychiatric affiliation at Alberta Hospital, Edmonton, instead of Ponoka. By 1966, the pediatric affiliation at the University of Alberta Hospital was increased to three months from two, so that the students could receive lectures at the same time as their posting. The Class of '66 was also the last class to affiliate at the Baker Sanatorium in Calgary (and the first one to graduate from the Morley Young Hall). Other specialties were taken at the Archer Memorial Hospital itself. These included clinic, operating room, public health, and diet kitchen.

1966 A.M.H. YEARBOOK

Candid shots abound in the yearbooks of the late 1960's. There was no identification of participants below many of the photos. Perhaps there was a good reason...

For the nursing students, physical life in residence was better than the earlier years of water shortages and cold rooms. The yearbooks throughout the late 1960's are full of student activities, with many candid shots that would suggest a close knit group of young women who shared many memorable moments together. Rituals such as initiation, capping, banding/band-raising, and graduation were woven together with corn roasts, Halloween and Christmas parties, variety nights and curling bonspiels. Student Government gave the nurses a chance to become familiar with their upcoming professional responsibilities.

Gail Goddard (Class of '63) received the Judge Hugh Farthing Bursary of the Tuberculosis Veterans' Association of the Canadian Legion for the best case study and highest marks of affiliating students at the Baker Sanatorium in 1962. Maurine Gillespie (Class of '64), and her husband Ray Holcomb, went to Gabon, Africa in 1970 as missionaries. They became involved in a number of different ministries, including children's care, home nursing and work at the Bongolo Evangelical Hospital.

In 1967, the Lamont-Mundare-Willingdon Hospital District was set up, creating new administrative processes. Construction began in August, 1969 on a 31 bed Nursing Home facility which was attached to the Auxiliary Hospital and shared a number of services (including administration, dietary, physiotherapy and recreation). There were soon to be four Health facilities at Lamont (The Archer, the Auxiliary Hospital, the Nursing Home, and the Senior Citizen's Lodge). In September, 1969, Dr. Young expressed the view that the development of a Joint Board for these facilities would be worth considering, and a committee was formed to examine the options.

In November, 1969, a motion came from the Hospital Board to set up a committee to consider the recent decision made by Directors of the Schools of Nursing in Alberta to favour a two-year in-college program for the education of nurses, replacing the existing three-year in-hospital training program. Dr. Young and Miss James met with Miss Margaret Steed, Advisor to Schools of Nursing, who suggested that the Archer Memorial Hospital was not positioned well enough to gain approval for a two-year program. A lack of community resources and strong faculty were cited, as well as the fact that changes occurring at the Alberta Hospital and University Hospital programs might not be suitable for Lamont. Discussions as to the future of the training school at Lamont were now under way, with the recommendation that the school make what improvements it could in the light of developing trends and revised regulations.

As this quote from Connie Omoth (Class of '71) brings out so clearly, the 1960's were a time of tremendous change. "Looking back on the 'Swinging Sixties' one views them with mixed emotions. This was the decade of moon walks and the heart transplants, the peppermint twist and the Miles for Millions, the Just Society and the Kennedy-King assassinations... paved streets in Lamont and unrestricted hours in residence. It marked the dawn of "Youth Power" in America; the students of the new generation are demanding freedom and change. We as nursing students have suggested, fought for and adapted to changes in the medical profession and in our way of life – our life in the nurses' residence." New freedoms may have been gained, but adapting to change would become a way of life for these young women, as well as those in more senior positions. A challenge for all was ahead.

AMH ARCHIVES

Archer Memorial Hospital in the 1970's

CHAPTER 8
1970 TO 1979

THE CHALLENGE OF CHANGE

With all the flurry of 1960's building activity at the Archer Memorial Hospital behind, and the prospect of a change in the School of Nursing looming on the horizon, the decade of the 1970's dawned with many questions about the future – a future which was somehow less sure and predictable than it had been. The pace of change seemed to have increased, requiring continual adjustments in philosophy, policy, procedures, and practice. "How to keep pace?" was a question that was being asked at all levels at the Archer Memorial Hospital.

Nowhere was this more evident than in the minutes of the Board. Throughout 1970 and 1971, extensive discussions and negotiations ensued about the future of the School of Nursing. Rising costs, difficulties in securing staff, changes in training regulations and requirements, and advances in the medical and nursing fields all affected the outcome of this decision.

Finally, at a special meeting of the Board on July 19, 1971 a motion was passed stating that those students who had applied for admission to the Fall, 1971 class be advised of the difficulties in securing adequate staff, and that "in due course and in an orderly manner, the Archer Memorial Hospital School of Nursing be phased out." A final graduation would be held on Saturday, June 24, 1972. (The class of 1973 was transferred to the University of Alberta School of Nursing in September, 1971.) Dr. Young's words described the response to this new turn of events, when he wrote "It is with regret and a deep feeling akin to nostalgia that this fact is recorded."

Although the School of Nursing would be closing, other aspects of medical care in the Lamont community were moving forward. The Nursing Home was completed in May, 1970, with the first admissions on June 18, 1970. Its official opening was held on June 17, 1971. The building, physically linked to the Auxiliary Hospital, shared a number of services such as administration, nursing, dietary, plant operation and maintenance, physiotherapy and recreation. Mr. John Matwichuk was named Administrator and Mrs. Margaret Frey was named Director of Nursing for both the Lamont Auxiliary Hospital and the Nursing Home.

The Senior Citizen's Lodge, known as Beaverhill Pioneer Lodge, was opened around this same time.

Long standing service by employees was recognized as an important contribution to the hospital, and due recognition was given to employees such as Leon Townsend who retired on July 31, 1970, at the age of 73 years, after 34 years of service as the Hospital's Chief Plant Engineer.

AMH ARCHIVES

The Nursing Home (above) and the Senior Citizen's Lodge (below) were opened in the early 1970's to meet the needs of a growing population of elderly people in the Lamont area

AMH ARCHIVES

LPH/AMH ALUMNAE ARCHIVES

The last class to graduate from the Archer Memorial Hospital School of Nursing, 1972

Sincere efforts were made to create a celebration for the final graduates of the Archer Memorial Hospital that would be comparable to all those that had preceded them. The Auditorium was packed with grads, family, and friends for the ceremony, followed by the customary post-graduation refreshments served by the Women's Auxiliary. A dinner and dance followed in the evening. The Alumnae Association had made the weekend into a homecoming and some three hundred Alumnae members attended the weekend events.

On Sunday June 25, 1972, recognition was given to the sixtieth anniversary of the School of Nursing, and to its closure. A pancake breakfast, church service, luncheon, singsong on the wards of the hospital, and afternoon program in the auditorium rounded out the day.

Dr. Young records that, "'I just cannot believe it' was an expression heard from many of those in attendance. Another era had come to an end."

To celebrate the closure of the school, a final yearbook was compiled which traced the history of the hospital and its nurses' training program over sixty years. Many of the early photographs are captured here, as well as a class photo of each of the graduating classes. As "The Lamp is Golden" contributed to the historical records of the hospital at its fiftieth anniversary, so also did this final yearbook at its sixtieth. It gave an insight into the pride, strength and memories that flowed from what had been created so many years before.

Changes continued, with the retirement of Miss Ethel James from the position of Director of Nursing, at the end of June, 1972. She was succeeded by Miss A.J. Lawrence, with Mrs. Bernice Schneider assisting.

This was not a hastily arrived at decision but followed many months of discussions related to modern trends in nursing education, facilities for clinical experience at our hospital, the cost of the program and the problem of getting adequately prepared school faculty.

The present trend in nursing education is toward a two-year program centered in a college or other educational institution. Schools of Nursing are being encouraged to seek more community experiences for their students. Psychology and Sociology are being stressed along with family planning, geriatric nursing, rehabilitative programs and more detail related to retarded and autistic children.

It is necessary for a school to be situated within reach of facilities which can offer these experiences and to have a prepared and experienced staff who can develop a program which offers them.

– Ethel C. James,
Director of Nursing,
in a newsletter to the
Alumnae of L.P.H. and A.M.H.

AMH ARCHIVES

Dr. M.A.R. Young, Charles Whittaker and Evelyn Lopetinsky enjoyed the 60th Anniversary Celebrations, June 24, 1972

ELLIS OBERLE

Dr. J.E. Hutson, arrived 1973

In March, 1973, Dr. John Edward Hutson was given privileges at the hospital. His specialty was the area of anaesthetics, a welcome addition of skills to the Medical Staff. He joined Drs. Young, Weatherilt, Dobson, Sunley, Wollard and Gutter (radiologist) as Active Medical Staff. The need for a second surgeon on staff was expressed at this same time, so work began to secure the appointment of an additional staff member.

The Board of the Archer Memorial Hospital was busy during this time with many issues regarding finances and future plans. Because the Archer was a "voluntary" institution under the auspices of the United Church of Canada, the recovery of financial costs was an ever-present concern. With the election success of the Progressive Conservatives in 1971 came changes to provincial funding, leaving the "Non-District" hospital with complications regarding the recovery of funds for operating deficits. "Voluntary Agreements" were subsequently put in place between the hospital and the surrounding municipalities, which reflected the use of the hospital's services by the communities it served. The Government also came to an agreement with respect to the owner's equity portion invested in the hospital (in this case the United Church of Canada), and made available a percentage of return on this investment. This was used to cover extraordinary building repair costs. Both of these changes eased what had been emerging as a considerable financial strain on the Archer Hospital.

The Women's Auxiliary of the Lamont Hospitals approached the Board for permission to install a stained glass panel in memory of Mrs. Jessie W. Archer, and Mrs. Ethel B. Young. The panel, placed in the front entrance of the Archer Memorial Hospital, was dedicated on November 4, 1973. It was a tangible recognition of these two women's contributions to the life and work of Lamont's hospital.

Mrs. Archer's contributions as anaesthetist at the hospital were almost legendary, but Mrs. Young's legacy was less well known. She was a graduate of Montreal General Hospital, and was Assistant Superintendent of the Montreal Maternity Hospital for several years before moving west with Morley in 1922. For 48 years she continued to offer help and advice to organizations connected with the hospital and School of Nursing. She was a Charter member, a President/Past President and an Honorary Life member of the Hospital Women's Auxiliary, as well as an Honorary Member of the Alumnae Association. She also welcomed student nurses into the Young home, encouraging those who found becoming a student nurse a challenging task.

KIRK HARROLD

Stained glass memorial to Jessie Archer and Ethel Young

On March 30, 1973, Chief Judge Nelles Buchanan resigned from the hospital Board, after 30 years in that office. In recognition of his contribution to Archer Memorial Hospital the minutes state that "His wise counsel and effective guidance of the affairs of Archer Memorial Hospital have been of a nature well beyond the call of duty." Mr. R.B. Christie assumed the position of Board Chairman, and Mr. Kent Harrold became Vice-Chairman.

LPH/AMH ALUMNAE ARCHIVES

Dr. Morley A.R.Young FRCS, FACS was the recipient of the honorary degree Doctor of the University of Calgary (DUC) at Convocation, at the University of Calgary, June 1, 1973

Dr. Young also received further recognition in June, 1973, when he was the recipient of an honorary degree from the University of Calgary. Dean W.A. Cochrane of the Faculty of Medicine presented the award to Dr. Young with these words, "Dr. Young represents the highest qualities of a family physician. He not only gave the highest quality of medical service to the people of Alberta, he also gave leadership to the community in the development of overall health services for the people of Alberta and Northern Saskatchewan."

In response to a *Commission Bulletin* from the Alberta Hospital Services Commission issued in 1972, a Joint Planning Committee was set, to act in an advisory capacity in developing plans for the future. The committee's first meeting was held February 19, 1974, with Mr. Kent Harrold nominated as Chairman. Its first order of business was to conduct a survey of residents and make recommendations for the future. One of those recommendations was to explore the setting up of a Preventive Social Services office in Lamont.

Another new program that was made available was a Ward Aide Inservice course. Mrs. Shirley Harrold, Director of Nursing Services at the Auxiliary and Nursing Home, worked with Miss A. Lawrence, Director of Nursing at the Archer Memorial Hospital, and Mrs. Sheila Sunley, Instructor, along with various adult education personnel to create a course at Lamont that was patterned after the one offered as a pilot program in 1972 at W.P. Wagner School, Edmonton. Lamont's course ran for 17 weeks, graduating 31 students on June 15, 1973.

AMH ARCHIVES

Mrs. Sheila Sunley, Instructor, with the graduates of the Ward Aide class, 1973

For the record: Fourteen sets of sisters attended the School of Nursing at Lamont, and six families had various combinations of mother/daughter/daughter-in-laws attend throughout the years.

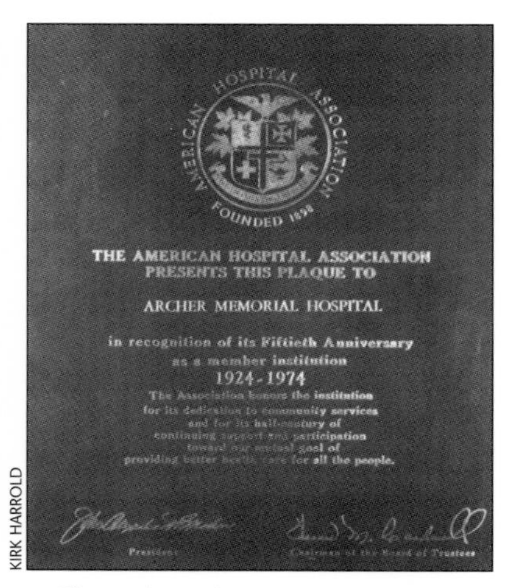

KIRK HARROLD

Plaque from the American Hospital Association, honouring 50 years of Lamont's membership in the Association

On May 2, 1973, twenty-two young people of the Lamont district graduated as "Volunteens" from a special program initiated by Miss Lawrence, in accord with the Canadian Red Cross Society's Volunteer Health Services Program. The Women's Auxiliary provided the new, pale blue official smocks that would be worn by the Vounteens when they were on duty assisting hospital staff.

Accreditation had been a long-standing source of pride for the hospital, and recognition of this accomplishment was forthcoming in October, 1974, when the American Hospital Association sent a plaque commemorating fifty years of membership in the association. During the 1975-76 year, the accreditation of Archer Memorial Hospital was limited to one year's approval instead of the usual three, pending compliance with recommendations set out by the accreditation surveyors. Two-year accreditation status was reinstated in 1977, and three-year status in 1979.

Several other changes occurred to various aspects of the hospital and its operation. Landscaping was completed around the hospital and Nurses' Residence. The ambulance entrance was remodeled and recemented to provide easier access to the ambulance, which was purchased September 11, 1974, and put into service immediately. The windows of the '28 and '48 wings were replaced with new aluminum windows, and the roof underwent repairs. Painting of the hospital was carried on under a maintenance program, while the fire escape at the north end of the 1948 wing was replaced completely. The food services of the hospital, which had been contracted to Versafoods from May, 1969, was reviewed in the early 1970's and all seemed to be working well (although the contract was eventually terminated in 1978).

By May, 1975 a separate emergency department had been set up on First Floor East. In May, 1976, at the request of the Lamont-Smoky Lake Auxiliary Hospital and Nursing Home District #23, 24 beds at the Archer Memorial Hospital were designated as Extended Care. On September 7, 1976, the new Extended Care Unit was opened, with 18 patients.

The presence of the United Church of Canada within the hospital was reaffirmed with the visitation of Dr. W. Donald Watt to the Board on January 23, 1975. Dr. Watt, as Superintendent of Hospital and Medical Work under the Division of Missions of the United Church of Canada, informed the Board of the work and facilities of the seven United Church hospitals across Canada. He also expressed that it was his feeling that the Church would continue with its hospital work.

AMH ARCHIVES

The Women's Auxiliary to the Lamont Hospitals continued to provide on-going support in the form of regular canteen services at A.M.H., the Auxiliary Hospital and the Nursing Home. The group also provided fund raising contributions for major purchases such as color televisions for the Auxiliary and Nursing Home

Retirements, resignations, and changes in staffing positions seemed to be the norm during this time. On the Medical Staff side, Dr. Lloyd Weatherilt retired in September, 1975. The Weatherilts moved to Edmonton where he became a Medical Officer for the Workers' Compensation Board. Dr. James McGill was granted privileges in 1976 and stayed until late 1977. Early in 1977, Dr. Mihir Ray arrived to add his expertise in surgery. Dr. Albert Dobson gave notice of his retirement as of July, 1977.

ELLIS OBERLE

Dr. M. Ray brought a surgical specialty to the medical staff, 1977

In December, 1975, Mrs. Bernice Schneider resigned her position as Associate Director of Nursing. Later in 1976, Miss A.J. Lawrence resigned as Director of Nursing, to be replaced by Mrs. E. McNamara. A number of nursing staff positions underwent revision during this time as well.

At the Board level, Mr. R.B. Christie resigned as Chairman of the Board in January, 1976, and Mr. Kent Harrold was then nominated to succeed him.

KIRK HARROLD

Kent Harrold, Board Chairman as of January, 1976

In a letter dated June 25, 1977, Dr. M.A.R. Young made the request to be relieved of " all definite administrative responsibility" due to declining health. The Board accepted Dr. Young's resignation as Administrator "with the greatest regret: in doing so the Board expressed its abiding affection for him as a person, its admiration of him as a physician and surgeon, its pride in him as an Administrator in the Hospital and Medical fields... and their thanks to him, that over a period of fifty five years he stayed with us, ignoring allurements elsewhere, serving this Hospital loyally, patients from three provinces devotedly, bringing distinction and undoubtedly, satisfaction both to himself and this Hospital." Both Dr. Young and Chief Judge Nelles V. Buchanan were made honorary life members of the Board in 1979. Mr. John Matwichuk was given the responsibilities of Administrator, after Dr. Young's letter.

Mrs. Donna Weatherilt was closely associated with the School of Nursing from 1949 to 1969. Much of her contribution was in the realm of teaching but at times she assumed supervisory responsibilities. She contributed much to the students and the School. Her efforts were very much appreciated.

– Alumnae newsletter, 1976

An unexpected event occurred with another letter presented to the Board in June, 1977, written by Dr. W. Donald Watt of the Division of Mission, United Church of Canada. The contents of this letter indicated that it was the decision of the Department of Church in Society that "responsibility for the operation of Archer Memorial Hospital be transferred from the Church to a Community or Municipal Board."

A request by Mrs. Bernice Schneider of the Alumnae Association to have a display cabinet built on the west wall of the Chapel to house the Alumnae Archives (photos, caps and other memorabilia) was granted. The Alumnae Association continued to function after the closure of the School of Nursing, bringing many long-time friends together to share memories and stories through their regular meetings and a newsletter.

Dr. W. Donald Watt came to the Board meeting June 14, 1977 to explain the reasons for the Church's new stand, and to seek correspondence or a petition citing reasons why the church should retain its involvement. A committee was formed immediately to respond to the issue, and the members created a "Statement of Concern", in reply to the Division of Mission's proposal to withdraw its sponsorship of the Archer Memorial Hospital. The Statement of Concern recognized 18 key points with regard to the presence of the Church in this Hospital, and concluded with a resolution asking the Division "to revoke its decision to withdraw from its association with Archer Memorial Hospital and that it continue the unique relationship which has been eminently successful in its results."

Dr. Watt further suggested at the April, 1978 Board meeting that the by-laws of the Hospital would need modifications to allow the church to have a greater say in the operation of the Hospital, and "to be certain that the high quality of service would continue in the future as has been provided in the past". A major thrust of the Board for the next while was aimed at making these by-law changes. Eventually there was a hold put on further decisions at the Division of Mission level, while these by-laws were reworked and other opinions sought about the role of the church in the hospital.

KIRK HARROLD

Dr. John Sunley appointed as Medical Superintendent, 1979

ELLIS OBERLE

Dr. Monica Johnson joined Lamont Clinic on November 1, 1978

ELLIS OBERLE

The blood bank service started in 1979, proved a valuable service for both emergencies and surgery

A request was also made by Dr. Watt to appoint a new Medical Superintendent for the Hospital. Dr. John Sunley was officially appointed in 1979.

An additional doctor was added to the Medical Staff in November, 1978, when Dr. Monica Johnson arrived at Lamont. Dr. Ray began to do gastroscopy work, and a blood transfusion service was instituted.

LAMONT AUXILIARY HOSPITAL ARCHIVES

LAMONT AUXILIARY HOSPITAL ARCHIVES

New forces were constantly adding impetus to change in the hospital and in the community. A meeting was held on April 6, 1978, which sixty people attended, to investigate the option of Home Care as a new service to the community. The very favorable response led to an Organizational Committee which was appointed to pursue this program. Meals on Wheels was later added to further meet the needs of people requiring assistance in their homes.

The Auxiliary Hospital and the Nursing Home continued to offer care for the aging population in the institutional setting. In late 1977, Lamont and Smoky Lake formed separate Auxiliary and Nursing Home Districts. The boards of the Archer Memorial Hospital and the Auxiliary and Nursing Home began discussions about the sharing of services, possibly through the construction of a connecting link between the two facilities. A feasibility study was approved to explore the options, and a joint meeting of the Boards came about on September 5, 1978, to discuss the issues. By December, 1979, negotiations were under way to share such services as laboratory, X-ray, and physiotherapy.

LAMONT AUXILIARY HOSPITAL ARCHIVES

Photos from the Auxiliary Hospital and Nursing Home scrapbook:

Top left: Patients enjoyed summer with a bar-b-que on the grounds of the hospital

Top centre: Yearly parade floats celebrated the Auxiliary Hospital and Nursing Home, often winning first prize in the local fair parade

Above: Christmas traditions were renewed each year through a pageant led by Sheila Sunley with residents as participants

LAMONT AUXILIARY HOSPITAL ARCHIVES

The Board members and staff of the Auxiliary Hospital stand beside a maxi-van donated in April, 1979, by the Associated Canadian Travellers (ACT) so that residents could participate in such community activities as shopping, visiting and touring Elk Island Park

LAMONT AUXILIARY HOSPITAL ARCHIVES

Mr. John Matwichuk retired, in 1979 after 33 years with the hospital

ELLIS OBERLE

Mr. Harold James, Administrator, and Mrs. Lynda Oberle, Director of Nursing, joined the staff in 1979

Mr and Mrs. Ralph Horley were appointed by the Alberta Conference of the United Church to look into the Church's involvement in the hospital, and to look at possible uses of the Nurses' Residence facility in the future. The Horleys visited the hospital September 18, 1979, and their report was to follow.

In keeping with the decade of change throughout the 1970's, 1979 was filled with changes at the management level of the hospital. Mr. John Matwichuk, after 33 years of service to the hospital, took retirement from his duties at the Archer in May, 1979, although he continued with his position as Administrator of the Auxiliary and Nursing Home. He was followed in September by Mrs. E. McNamara leaving her position as Director of Nursing, for a position closer to her home.

Two new faces appeared on the scene in late 1979. Mr. Harold James, who had served as charge technologist with the Laboratory Department for a time, completed the Hospital Administration and Health Care program through the University of Saskatchewan, and was appointed the new Administrator of the hospital. Mrs. Lynda Oberle, a University of Alberta graduate and now resident of Lamont, became the new Director of Nursing in November, 1979.

The work of these people in administering the hospital was ably supported by that of people like Mrs. Pearl Andrais and Mrs. Olga Paruk who provided important support services in the Business Department. Other departments of the hospital, such as Nursing and General Staff, were fortunate to have many members on staff who had been with the hospital for years. Dr. Young paid tribute to these people, saying the "their faithfulness and loyalty is much appreciated by our Board and pictorial recognition is found in the 1972 nurses' yearbook."

Once again, the Archer Memorial Hospital was poised to move into the future, having gone through yet another decade of major change. Celebrating sixty years of service; closing the training school; examining the Church's involvement; seeing the retirement of many long-standing, hard-working staff and administrative people; and adapting to new financial and structural realities made this a time of great challenge. But with new faces, a fresh focus on the future, and the ever-present dedication of the people at Archer Memorial Hospital and its neighboring facilities, the Auxiliary Hospital, Nursing Home and Senior Citizen's Lodge, health care at Lamont continued its traditional mission of serving the medical and spiritual needs of patients.

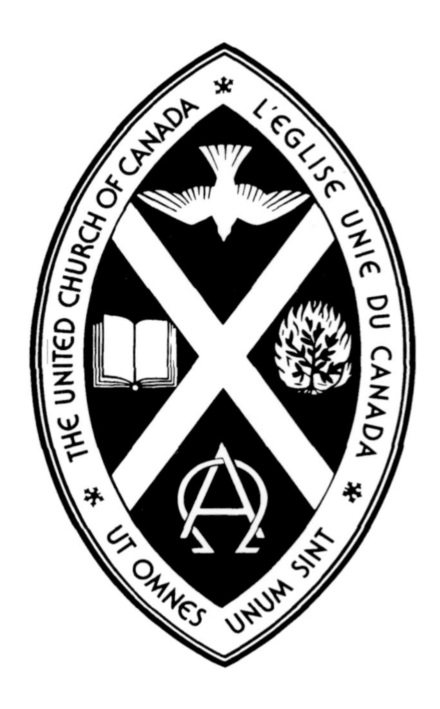

The Church Crest of the United Church of Canada, owner and operator of the Archer Memorial Hospital

CHAPTER 9
1980 TO 1989
A DREAM OF COMMUNITY HEALTH CARE

Taking care of the spiritual needs of patients was an important component of the medical work at the Archer Memorial Hospital. Throughout its long association with the United Church of Canada, the emphasis had been on meeting not only the physical needs of patients but also psychological, emotional and spiritual needs of the whole person. Because the "holistic" approach to health care was valued, there was always an emphasis on finding better ways to meet the varied needs of patients, staff and administration, within a caring environment.

The relationship between the United Church of Canada and the Archer Memorial Hospital was examined when the Horley Report to the United Church Conference was presented on February 13, 1980, with the recommendation that the church's link with the hospital be concluded. The Alberta Conference Executive, however, decided to recommend to the Division of Mission in Canada that the long-standing relationship between church and hospital should be continued, and that further efforts be made to find a meaningful role for the facilities at Lamont.

LAMONT AUXILIARY HOSPITAL ARCHIVES

Pastoral Care has always been a part of the Archer Memorial Hospital's mandate. Clergy from a range of ecumenical traditions came to tend to the spiritual needs of patients at the hospital.

In September, 1980, a meeting of the clergy in the Lamont vicinity was held to discuss cooperation in the delivery of pastoral care and worship services for the patients of Archer Memorial Hospital, the Auxiliary and Nursing Home, and the residents of the Beaverhill Pioneer Lodge. The Ukrainian Greek Catholic, Roman Catholic, Lutheran, Moravian and United Churches were represented at the meeting, and a Pastoral Care Program was established. A schedule was set up with one denomination responsible for the services each week to which people of all faiths were invited. A list of clergy would circulate to staff, in order that patients and families could contact the clergy of their choice. Outreach to staff would also be made through the provision of regular morning devotions.

Another way that the hospital worked to meet the needs of its patients and staff was to establish efficient departments and nursing units. During the early 1980's, each department reported to the Board, discussing new equipment needs, staffing, regulatory requirements, and issues such as computerization. This gave an opportunity for Board members to become familiar with each department's functions and for departments to bring forward concerns or needs. Open Houses were also instituted during this time to help familiarize the community with the workings of the hospital.

AMH ARCHIVES

L. "Bud" Haverstock, Pharmacy Department

In the Pharmacy, L. "Bud" Haverstock managed the routines of the department: filling daily orders, stocking medications, purchasing inventory, and monitoring the use of medications and new products that became available from pharmaceutical companies. He shared his time with the Auxiliary and Nursing Home, and offered inservice lectures on topics of interest to staff. Bud considered the future in his report to the Board in 1980: " I can look into my crystal ball and see computerization – both for patient profiles and formulary compilation – in fact the latter area is being considered at the present time." A computer in the pharmacy was a few years away, but it did become a reality by 1985.

Gloriann Sarafinchin, assisted by Adeline Gurba, maintained responsibility for the Medical Records Department of the hospital. In her report to the Board in 1980, she explained that medical records was the "who, what, why, where, when and how of a patient's care during hospitalization." She went on to say that these records were used to communicate among medical staff, nurses and paramedical staff, to provide data for use in research and education, and to provide a measure for the review of health care services in the institution. A policy on confidentiality and retention of medical records guided the use of and access to the records.

AMH ARCHIVES

Gloriann Sarafinchin,
Medical Records Department

Ann Kendall arrived in 1979 to begin work in the X-ray Department at the Archer Memorial Hospital. Her co-workers in 1981 included Emily Doskoch, Anita Anderson, Sonia Mackay and Vida Laschuk. Dr. Gutter continued to offer his services as radiologist, a position he had held since 1952. With the addition of a new automatic film processing unit, and the installation of a new X-ray machine (with the capacity to do tomography) in January, 1981, the efficiency of the department was much improved.

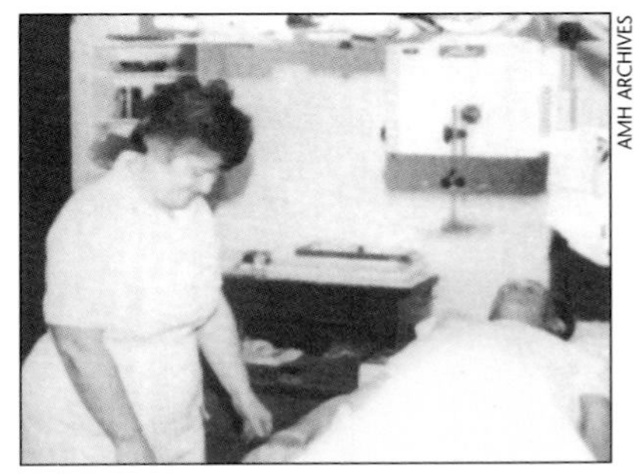

AMH ARCHIVES

Ann Kendall, Radiology Department

Laboratory Services were another integral part of the hospital, providing diagnostic services such as clinical chemistry, urinalysis, microbiology, hematology and histology investigations. It also had responsibility for the provision of electrocardiograms (ECG's). The Blood Bank, started in 1979, had become an important service at the Archer Memorial with lab technicians now able to provide matched blood for transfusion within 20-30 minutes. Laboratory staff throughout the early 1980's included Sherry Salton, David Stahl, Roseann Herchek, Margaret Dupas and Blanche Dembicki.

Support services, which were a necessary part of the hospital, came from the Administration Office, Dietary Department, Plant Operation and Maintenance, Housekeeping and Laundry. A security service was later put in place to ensure the safety of the premises, patients, visitors and staff. The staff in these departments worked equally as hard behind the scenes for the Archer Memorial Hospital as other, more visible staff. New faces appeared, such as Dolores Sadoway in the Administration Office. Other individuals took on new responsibilities, such as Olga Paruk who became Business Manager in 1984, replacing Pearl Andrais who retired after 31 years service.

Doctors from other hospitals in the region were granted privileges at the Archer Memorial, as Courtesy or Consulting Medical Staff, while two dentists came from Fort Saskatchewan to spend one day per week providing routine dental services to the community as well as doing dental surgery in the operating room.

The hospital purchased capital equipment for the various departments during the early 1980's, which included an anaesthetic machine, a Wright's Respirometer, a "crash cart" with monitor and defibrillator, and other equipment to upgrade or extend the services available from each department. Community donations were also an important part of this process. The Womens' Auxiliary to the Lamont Hospitals made a contribution to a new incubator and the local Lions Club partially funded a fibre-optic sigmoidoscope. In recognition of donations and bequests, a large bronze plaque was placed in the entrance to the hospital.

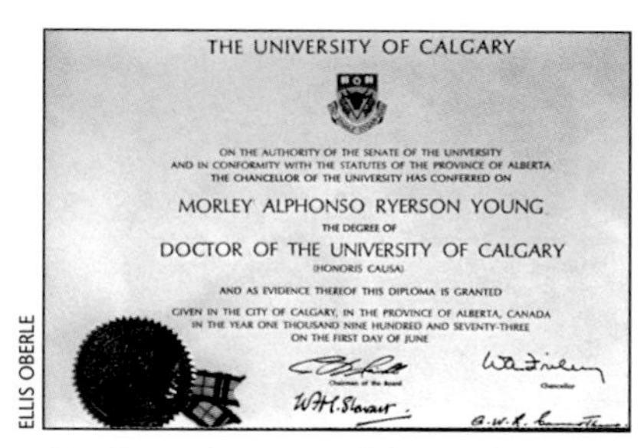

THE UNIVERSITY OF CALGARY

ON THE AUTHORITY OF THE SENATE OF THE UNIVERSITY
AND IN CONFORMITY WITH THE STATUTES OF THE PROVINCE OF ALBERTA
THE CHANCELLOR OF THE UNIVERSITY HAS CONFERRED ON

MORLEY ALPHONSO RYERSON YOUNG

THE DEGREE OF

DOCTOR OF THE UNIVERSITY OF CALGARY

(HONORIS CAUSA)

AND AS EVIDENCE THEREOF THIS DIPLOMA IS GRANTED

GIVEN IN THE CITY OF CALGARY, IN THE PROVINCE OF ALBERTA, CANADA
IN THE YEAR ONE THOUSAND NINE HUNDRED AND SEVENTY-THREE
ON THE FIRST DAY OF JUNE

Chairman of the Board

Chancellor

ELLIS OBERLE

Dr. Young's memorabilia, such as this diploma from the University of Calgary, were gathered into an archive at the hospital

Nursing services were enriched by a strong inservice program. Case studies, instruction in the use of new equipment, and discussions by doctors from the Lamont Clinic and other professionals were some of the topics available.

For the first time ever, the general duty nurses went on strike at the Archer Memorial Hospital during April, 1980. In a "Report from the Archer Memorial Hospital" the following comments by an unknown writer give some insight into the strike: "A strike experience is not pleasant; one senses a feeling of indignity in such a confrontation. We did not have any so-called 'unpleasant incidents' in the conduct of people involved in the strike but the feeling of uneasiness at seeing people you have worked with so closely and for many continuous years, parading with signs and pickets expressing dissatisfaction and discontent, was definitely felt by those of us in administration and management."

KIRK HARROLD

A playschool program used the Nurses' Residence facilities two half days per week

A second strike was held in early 1982. During the 23 day strike, the hospital at Lamont stayed open for emergencies and maternity cases, while two other hospitals in the region were closed by the strike. Nursing services were provided by very dedicated administration, nurse managers and nursing aides, until regular services were restored.

New trends, such as the nurses' strike, stood in sharp contrast to the decline of old familiar people and places that was occurring at the same time. Dr. Young was unable to attend the February, 1981, Board meeting because he was confined to bed. Dr. Young then passed away on April 15, 1981, at the age of 86 years. In honor of his many accomplishments it was decided that an archive would be established at the Archer Memorial Hospital which would house Dr. Young's writings, diplomas and certificates (32 in total), his prescription book from his early days in Lamont, robes he wore as President of the Canadian Medical Association and other items of interest from Dr. Young's life. Antique operating room equipment and old hospital supplies rounded out the archive collection.

The 1982 edition of the Alumnae Newsletter was dedicated to "the memory of our beloved Dr. Morley A.R. Young (Lamont 1922-1981) whose life was 'his hospital', his family, his girls (graduates of L.P.H. and A.M.H.), his deep concern, and care, for all who had the privilege of knowing him and of serving with him. Each one of us have special memories of how this great man's talent touched our life to help guide us in our chosen profession. He was honored by many but he always remained our friend, our Dr. Young."

The Nurses' Residence was undergoing a significant change in its use. It was still being used in several ways, although not to capacity. Various United Church Conference and Presbytery Committees used the facilities for meetings and provincial functions. Community groups rented the facilities on a yearly basis for programs such as a kindergarten program two days per week, a playschool program two half days per week, and a Public Health Office one day per week. The Nechi Institute on Drug and Alcohol Education and The Alberta Indian Health Care Commission used the facilities for a training program that began in September, 1981, and ran for nearly two years. Programs to accommodate clinical experiences for Grant MacEwan students, R.N.A.'s from Alberta Vocational College, and clinical experiences for B.Sc.N. students at the University of Alberta were made available, using the residence to house students when needed.

LPH/AMH ALUMNAE ARCHIVES

Florence Love, a life member of the Alumnae Association, officially opened the archives of the Alumnae Association, June 6, 1982

Before the "Dr. Young Archives" was opened in November, 1984, the "Alumnae Archives" had their official opening in conjunction with the 70th anniversary of the hospital. The event on Sunday June 6, 1982, was well attended by many alumnae, who came to enjoy a church service at the Lamont United Church Sunday morning, followed by lunch at the Christian Education Centre and the singing of hymns in the hospital corridor. An open house at the Archer Memorial was followed by the official opening of the Alumnae Archives. The Alumnae Association later celebrated with their annual dinner event at the new Lamont Curling Rink, attended by over 90 members.

LPH/AMH ALUMNAE ARCHIVES

Bernice Schneider and L. Marie Young at the ribbon-cutting to celebrate the opening of the Alumnae Archives, June 6, 1982. Behind them is a photo display of all the graduating classes from the School of Nursing, 1912-1972

While both the Alumnae Archives and the Dr. Young Archives were an opportunity to "look back" at history, a Long Range Planning Committee of the hospital board was beginning the process of "looking forward" to the future. According to the board minutes, "This special committee was appointed in 1981. Members of this committee acted as a special Ad Hoc Committee dealing with proposals to expand the hospital and enrich the Extended Care program at the Archer Memorial Hospital. Although this expansion request was denied, Mr. James encouraged the Board to appoint such a committee, so that services now being provided by the Archer Memorial Hospital could be reviewed and evaluated further. By so doing community health needs could be reviewed and assessed."

Reviewing and assessing was the next step. To renovate or replace the physical facilities, especially those built in 1948, became a pressing question for the Long Range Planning Committee. The Administrator's report to the Board in March, 1983, cited broken pipes, cracked flooring, uneven distribution of heat, poor ventilation, and deteriorating walls as some of the problem areas. By April, 1984, a motion was made that, because of the age of the 1948 wing and its structural deficiencies, a request be initiated for a detailed assessment by the Department of Hospitals and Medical Care. The wheels were set in motion for another change at the Archer.

Medical students had been welcomed throughout the years at the Lamont Public/Archer Memorial Hospital, and during the summers of 1980 and 1981 medical students from Glasgow University spent a four or six week internship here and were pleased with the practical experience they gained. In 1982, two students from Ontario, on one and two month electives, were at the Archer Memorial Hospital.

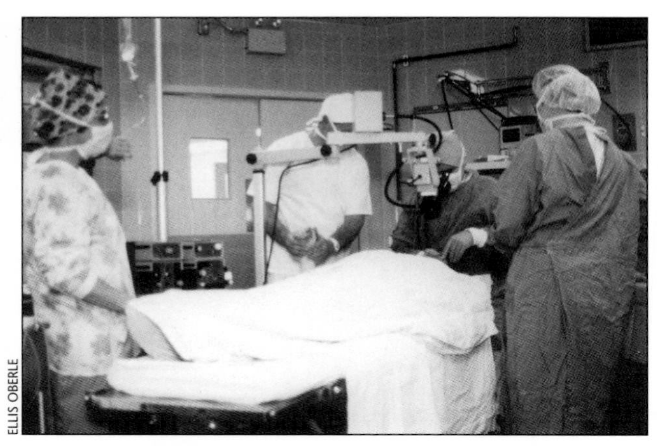

ELLIS OBERLE

Dr. Ross Harris,
Ophthalmology Program

KIRK HARROLD

Fair Booth at Lamont Sports
Days Trade Fair, 1985

In another positive direction, two new services were added to the Archer in the mid 1980's. The hospital's Ambulance Committee entered into negotiations with the Local Authorities to purchase a new, fully-equipped ambulance in March, 1983, to serve the district. Based at the Archer Memorial Hospital, the new ambulance went into service almost immediately, using the old ambulance as a backup. This service remained active until a change-over in 1988 to a private ambulance contractor.

Dr. Ross Harris, an ophthalmologist from Sherwood Park, was granted privileges at the hospital in 1985, bringing with him an ophthalmology program that was a first of its kind for the Archer.

"Fiscal restraint" was becoming a new part of everyone's vocabulary, as the high interest rates and high wage settlements of the early eighties took their toll of budgetary allocations. Harold James, Administrator at the Archer Memorial Hospital, had the difficult task of juggling the many needs, requests and policies of departments, doctors, staff, and government. He proved so capable that he was asked to take on the administration of the Auxiliary Hospital and the Nursing Home as well, which he did in 1984.

Attention to public relations was another trend that emerged during this time. Lower occupancy rates at the hospital prompted examination of the perceptions of the community in relation to the hospital. A Patient Care Committee was set up, to administer a questionnaire to in- and out-patients to determine their level of satisfaction with the services they had received. A four-page newsletter was approved for distribution to the community, and a column in the newspaper was initiated to raise awareness of the hospital and its services. The hospital also manned a booth at the Sports Day Trade Fair at Lamont, reaching many people through displays and personal contact. The Director of Nursing, Lynda Oberle, remarked later that she and her nursing staff and board volunteers did 210 blood pressures and 125 blood glucose checks over the three days of the display.

In 1984 a major historical project was begun by the Alumnae Association, initiated by Florence Love. It was her wish to have a biography written for each of the nurses who had graduated from the Lamont School of Nursing, 1912-1972. The stories would be compiled into a book format and become part of the Alumnae Archives. The books were to be dedicated at the 75th Anniversary of the Archer Memorial Hospital in 1987. Shirley Harrold (Class of '51) and Fran Nelson (Class of '70) headed the project

Meanwhile, the assessment of the physical facilities was pursued, with Alastair Cockburn, Architect, providing a detailed review of the current conditions of the buildings. His report looked at four areas- architectural, mechanical, electrical and structural, then made five recommendations regarding Fire Code and Safety Upgrades and the renovation or replacement of the physical facilities. The Board of the Archer Memorial Hospital decided unanimously to accept Option 5, which was to make an application to appropriate government officials for a new facility.

Even with an intent to move towards a new facility, Fire Code and Safety Upgrades were required on the present facilities to keep them in service. The Nursing Home underwent its upgrade in October, 1984, at a cost of $172,882, with the Auxiliary Hospital during 1985-1986 at a cost of $332,650. In November, 1985, the Archer Memorial Hospital received $800,000 to undertake its Safety and Environmental upgrading project.

In early 1986, the Archer Memorial Hospital received a significant bequest from the will of Catherine Jennie Harper. Interest from this investment was used to purchase additional equipment for special purposes, such as a blood pressure monitor, and a phacoemulsification machine for the ophthalmology program. Her contribution was greatly appreciated.

Although the upgrades necessitated an attitude of patience on everyone's part while the renovations went on, Dr. Sunley spoke about the upgrading at the Archer in a positive light when he said, "There have been disruptions and some curtailment of activity but with cooperation and ingenuity, the Hospital has remained operational. We have taken the opportunity afforded by the disruption to alter and rearrange some of the functions within the Hospital; e.g. labour and delivery room in the former recovery room [next] to the O.R., and the old case room becomes a non-smoking dayroom. All surgery and obstetrics will be on first floor, medicine, pediatrics and extended care on second floor."

LAMONT AUXILIARY HOSPITAL ARCHIVES

A celebration in 1989 marked the 25th Anniversary of the Lamont Auxiliary Hospital

Discussions between the Archer Memorial Hospital Long Range Planning Committee, the Lamont Auxiliary Hospital and Nursing Home District Board, and other community agencies such as the Vegreville Health Unit Board began to lay the foundations for the concept of a community health care centre. Meetings concentrated on reviewing programs offered by each of the players, reviewing shared service provisions, and establishing a long-term project that would meet the health care needs of the community. A Capital Project Request, covering a statement of the problem, a history and scope of services, supporting data, and alternative solutions was approved and sent to the Minister of Hospitals and Medical Care as of March, 1985.

LAMONT AUXILIARY HOSPITAL ARCHIVES

Inter-hospital Christmas parties gave staff the opportunity to mix in a social setting

LAMONT AUXILIARY HOSPITAL ARCHIVES

Residents Mrs. Lopushinsky and Anne Andruchow caught up on their visiting while sitting in the sunshine

June 27, 1986, marked the 25th anniversary of Dr. Sunley's work at the Archer Memorial Hospital. Harold James commended Dr. Sunley for his dedication and thanked him for being a good physician and a good friend.

The United Church decided in 1985 to set up a Task Force to examine the role of the Division of Mission and Service in medical work. A review at this level of the United Church had not been conducted since the 1950's. Composed of five to six people with expertise in such areas as theology, bio-ethics, social systems, nursing, psychiatry, and community development, the Task Force would develop a policy statement and plan of action for the United Church's involvement in health services in Canada. Dr. Sunley, in his greetings to the Alumnae in 1986, said, "The recommendations of this Task Force will undoubtedly have a profound effect on all the United Church Hospitals, and hopefully will clarify where the United Church is going in terms of its medical work." Two members of this committee, Dr. Peter Newbery and Miss Elaine Kaye visited Lamont in September, 1986, to meet with staff, physicians, Board members, and community people to gain some perspective on the church-run hospital in this community.

The role of Chaplain at the Archer Memorial was expanded in the early part of 1986, through the efforts of the Board. Although an unsuccessful application was made to the United Church for funding for this new position, the Board still considered it important enough to go ahead, funding it from its own discretionary resources. The new minister of the United Church, Rev. Tom McLaughlin, agreed to take on the role of Hospital Chaplain. He spent one day a week at the hospital, was included in patient rounds, and offered daily devotions for staff.

DORIS ANDRAIS

Archer Memorial Hospital Board of Management, 1987. Left to right, back: Doris Andrais, Dr. John Sunley, Kent Harrold, Joe Hrycyk,Henry Kowalchuk, Peter Zagrosh. Left to right, front: Doris Shortt, Rev. Tom McLaughlin, Rev. Jim Shortt, Ed Stelmach, Harold James. Missing: Anelia Topolnisky

The Board of the Archer Memorial Hospital at this time was made up of seven representatives appointed by the United Church, five representatives from the County, and the President of the Women's Auxiliary to the Hospitals. Mr. Kent Harrold continued to receive a vote of confidence from the Board in his on-going re-election to the position of Chairman. Dr. Sunley paid tribute to Mr. Harrold's role as Chairman when he moved the following: "A vote of thanks to Mr. Kent Harrold for the fine job he does as Chairman of this Board. Kindly and fair control of the meeting, directing the discussion, being diplomatic – all of these and many more things could be said of the way Kent does his task in the chair. I think all would agree when I say that Kent has the ability to make us all feel equally important, to make us feel we are contributing to the work of this group."

The need for an increase in long-term care beds was becoming apparent. During 1986, the Lamont Auxiliary Hospital was awarded a 25-bed expansion, if the Archer Memorial Hospital would close their 24 extended care beds. This was not viewed as a good solution to the problems of either the aging Archer Memorial Hospital or the Lamont Auxiliary Hospital, so the Boards decided to work together to address their mutual concerns.

Catching up on people:

- *Chief Judge Nelles V. Buchanan passed away at the end of 1986*
- *L. Marie Young returned to Lamont as a resident in the Auxiliary Hospital*
- *Harold James and Lynda Oberle completed the Central Michigan University Masters Program in Health Services Administration*
- *The position of Medical Superintendent underwent a revision and Dr. Ross Harris was appointed as Chief of Medical Staff*

Over the next while, discussions were ongoing as the Boards, in conjunction with outside consultative services, slowly worked towards the vision that emerged of an integrated community health care facility. Issues such as mission statements, equity, board composition, tours to other facilities, and revising submissions to government offices meant that the Planning Committee was very active during this time. A proposal for a new health care complex in Lamont was finally submitted to the Minister of Hospitals and Medical Care in June, 1987.

Meanwhile, another committee of the Board had been busy planning the 75th Anniversary event. The July 3-5, 1987 weekend celebrations included a special service of dedication at the Lamont United Church for the Alumnae history books, a banquet and dance, a pancake breakfast and closing ceremonies. Many memories were revived, many old friendships were renewed, and plans for the future capital project were shared.

KIRK HARROLD

The history books of the Alumnae Association were dedicated at the 75th Anniversary celebrations. Florence Love speaks to the gathering, while Shirley Harrold and Fran Nelson hold the books containing biographies of the nurses from the School of Nursing, 1912-1972

In the months after the anniversary celebrations, the medical staff at Lamont went through a significant transition, as Dr. J. Sunley resigned from his position as Medical Superintendent although remaining at the Lamont Clinic, while Dr. E. Hutson and Dr. M. Johnson moved on. Dr. M. Ray continued to offer surgery, Dr. E. Weins applied for Consulting privileges in General Surgery, Dr. R. Brown from Mundare increased his time at Lamont, and Dr. G. Lippolt arrived to offer his services in anaesthesia.

On March 25, 1988, after many months of planning and lobbying, the Honorable Marvin Moore and M.L.A. Steve Zarusky announced a capital project for Lamont. The project was announced as a 32-bed general hospital with 25 long-term care beds with expanded support and ambulatory care services, at a cost of $12.8 million (April, 1987 dollars).

KIRK HARROLD

The tradition of a Uniform Parade was upheld at the anniversary celebrations, as nurses model the changes in uniforms over 75 years

A slogan contest was held in 1989 by the Public Relations Committee. David Stahl created the winning slogan "A Mission in Progressive Health Care". It resonates with a statement from a paper relating the vision of the United Church Task Force on the future of the Archer Memorial Hospital: "The concept of a community health care centre encompassing all of the health related services for a rural community in one cooperatively operated centre emphasizing the healthy lifestyle approach for health care programs being developed by the Archer and Auxiliary Hospital Boards is an innovative plan."

The Boards faced a challenge, though. The Honorable Marvin Moore had, in the interests of cost cutting and operational efficiency, determined that if this new facility was to come about, it meant that there would need to be one Board, one management, and one health care centre structure. Amalgamation of the Boards was necessary. This process was initiated in June, 1989, and was to continue for several years of re-visioning, intense negotiations, staff input and public meetings.

On yet another front, the United Church Task Force gave their report to the Division of Mission and Service in Canada in April, 1987, reaffirming the role of the church in the provision of medical services in Canada. On January 17, 1989, a presentation was made by a group from the Archer Memorial Hospital to a United Church Consultation Group representing national, provincial and local levels of the church. A motion was passed recommending the continued role of the United Church of Canada in the hospital and retaining the church's on-going financial equity.

Before the next stages of the health care centre could take place, however, a major event had to occur. Since upgrading the Nurses' Residence was far too expensive, it was decided that the building would be demolished. An auction was held on August 19, 1989, to dispose of the furniture and small fixtures that could be reused.

Turning a dream into reality takes work, and the people who created these changes at the hospital in Lamont did not always find this an easy process. However, by the close of the 1980's, the dream of a community health care complex that was rooted in the Christian ethic of caring was on its way to becoming a reality.

An auction of furnishings from the Nurses' Residence was held in August, 1989

KIRK HARROLD

The demolition of the Nurses' Residence was accompanied by a strong feeling of sentiment in the community

CHAPTER 10

1990 TO 1999

FOUNDATIONS FOR THE FUTURE

Demolition of the Nurses' Residence was the next major step to be taken before plans for the new facility could proceed. Arrangements were made to salvage various furnishings, service equipment, and building supplies from the buildings and by January, 1990, both the Morley Young Hall and the Residence were demolished to make way for the new facility. All that remained of the dream from 1960 was a levelled area ready to be incorporated into the new plans.

On June 2,1991, the Alumnae Association dedicated two bronze plaques in memory of Dr. Young and Dr. Weatherilt, similar to the one created in memory of Dr. Alton. The plaques were placed in the hospital, to recognize the long-standing contributions of these doctors to both hospital and community.

Before the architect could proceed, however, a scope definition report had to be completed and submitted to the Government for approval. This report defined the total space to be incorporated in the new facility - 6650 square meters (about 66,500 square feet). Approval to proceed to the next stage in the building process was contingent upon the availability of funds from the government, but that decision was not forthcoming because of fiscal restructuring and government cutbacks.

By the fall of 1990, the operational funding crunch that affected many hospitals across the province had hit Lamont, where the deficit was projected to be $240,000. Salaries and supply/cost increases soon ate up any increases provided by the government and Lamont was forced to reduce services and make staffing changes to cope with the reduction in dollars. An article in a local newspaper dated October 2, 1990, indicates that Lamont had been able to keep staff job loss to only one position, by restructuring hours, trimming but not eliminating programs, and using other cost-cutting measures to balance the budget. The Board's commitment to avoid laying off people was a primary consideration in their approach to the problem.

LAMONT AUXILIARY HOSPITAL ARCHIVES

Scouts from the community took part in an "Adopt a Grandparent" activity in 1990

However, major refurbishing to the Lamont Auxiliary and Nursing Home was accomplished during the winter of 1990. With the support of government funding and funds from the Lamont Auxiliary Hospital and Nursing Home Board, new flooring, redesigned patient rooms and bathrooms, installation of heating and cooling systems, modifications to the rotunda and front entrance, as well as repairs to the roof and medical gas systems were accomplished. According to a report to the community, the renovations resulted in an "atmosphere that is much more conducive to work and we have no doubt that residents and staff are happy to be in the new improved environment." A ceremony to celebrate the completion of those renovations was held in December, 1990.

LAMONT AUXILIARY HOSPITAL ARCHIVES

Residents took a trip to Kananaskis Country in 1989. One resident had never seen the mountains before – he was delighted to finally have the chance on this trip

Later, a pedway was constructed between the Archer and Auxiliary hospitals to facilitate the movement of services and supplies. Long-term care residents could now be easily moved for diagnostic tests, clinic appointments and transfers. Dietary services and laundry were also able to be integrated more effectively. The pedway was funded by the Board of the Archer Memorial Hospital at a cost of $125,000.

LAMONT AUXILIARY HOSPITAL ARCHIVES

Long-time resident Annie Ulan enjoys special visitors

The process of amalgamating the Boards of the Archer Memorial Hospital and the Lamont Auxiliary and Nursing Home was now well underway. The first major block was cleared when the hospital district boundaries were declared "co-terminus". This meant that the geographical boundaries for the Lamont Auxiliary and Nursing Home District No. 23 became the same as those of Lamont General Hospital District No. 64. Ministerial approval was gained for the formation of the Lamont General and Auxiliary Hospital and Nursing Home District No. 23, and an Order-in-Council was passed on August 24, 1989, establishing the new district.

DORIS ANDRAIS

An official celebration of the Amalgamation of Boards was held September 1, 1992. The Honorable Nancy Betkowski, Minister of Health (seated centre) with Peter Zagrosh, (seated left), and Kent Harrold, (seated right). Left to right standing: Ed Stelmach, Richard Mandryk, Rev. Dave Edwards, Doris Andrais, Pat Hryniw, Violet Hackett, Mae Adamyk, Irene Inglis, Anelia Topolnisky, Rev. Jim Shortt

One of the tasks that the Joint Planning Committee was involved in during this time was reviewing the options by which the Boards could be amalgamated. The Archer Memorial Hospital was under the umbrella of the United Church of Canada, while the Lamont Auxiliary and Nursing Home was a District-run facility. Districts were determined and funded by the provincial government. Agreement was reached to form one Board from the two facilities, under the auspices of the United Church, with the District playing a major role. A consultant was hired to facilitate the transition, and a Strategic Plan was drawn up to guide the integration of services, departments and staff.

An Amalgamation Agreement was drafted, reconsidered, and reviewed by legal counsel, protecting the equity of both partners. After several drafts, the documents were approved by both Boards, and sent to the government in the spring of 1991. The agreement then went through bureaucratic reviews for an extensive period of time, while the Boards awaited the outcome. The Amalgamation Agreement finally received Ministerial approval in July, 1992, becoming effective on August 1, 1992. The new Lamont Health Care Centre was officially recognized.

Harold James, now Executive Director, stated that, "The most important thing we learned through this process was to communicate, communicate, communicate." Staff were consulted about the best ways to accomplish the integration of services and they were kept informed at all stages of the process. There were no staff layoffs as a result of the amalgamation and no staff member was asked to move from one facility to the other. Meetings were also held with the physicians to determine their needs and to enlist their cooperation.

It took a great deal of patience, understanding, expenses, tolerance, and perseverance on the part of the Committee members and certainly the going was not always smooth. However there was overall agreement that the primary focus was to strike an agreement that would enhance the overall health care for the community.

– Kent Harrold

LHCC

Jim Burger, Director of Finance

LHCC

Evelyn Lopetinsky,
Director of Nursing Services

A day patient in the recovery lounge after a lens implant said, " I don't know what I would have done without this hospital. My eyes were so bad I couldn't drive anymore, and I would have to wait another seven months to have this done anywhere else." The lens implant program enables about 200 people every year to resume a normally sighted life. The procedure is not funded by Alberta Health, and the Centre provided the nursing staff, operating theatre and lenses as a service to patients.

– Archer Memorial Hospital Support Group, 1992

Other important events were happening during the time of the amalgamation. Out of the amalgamation process came a Mission Statement that would form the foundation for the future at the Lamont Health Care Centre. The statement reads: "We believe that wholeness of body, mind, and spirit is God's will for every person. We commit ourselves to the promotion of health, the healing of illness, the care of the elderly and the disabled, and the well-being of the community."

Lamont also joined forces with three other hospitals in the area (Redwater, Mundare, and Fort Saskatchewan) to form the "Core Four" group, a regional planning network. Through these efforts, a more regionalized approach to services was established. These hospitals developed an Inventory of Services and a Role Statement to streamline the delivery of services, to lessen duplication and to provide a wider range of service options. For example, the mental health outreach services were offered out of Redwater, while Fort Saskatchewan's emergency department offered services after 7 p.m., when Lamont's emergency department closed for the night. The lens implant surgery program that had been established by Dr. Harris, and the laparoscopy surgery provided by Dr. Ray gave Lamont special services of its own.

Staffing changes were occurring as well, with the resignation of Lynda Oberle as Director of Nursing, who had accepted a new position. Her role was filled in November, 1991, by Evelyn Lopetinsky, whose position eventually became the Director of Nursing Services for the new Lamont Health Care Centre. Jim Burger became the Director of Finance for the Centre.

Among the doctors at the Lamont Clinic, there was what was called a "Medical Staff Manpower Shortage" at this time. Drs. Ray and Sunley carried a heavy load of care during this time, because Dr. Lippolt left in 1991. Dr. Patrick Wong arrived that same year to practice at Lamont, but was only here until early 1993 when he then moved to Calgary. Dr. Doug Stevens came to Lamont after Dr. Wong, but he too moved on after only a short time. The "Medical Staff Manpower Shortage" persisted.

On Sunday June 7, 1992, the 80th Anniversary of the hospital at Lamont was celebrated with a non-denominational church service at Lamont United Church, followed by a brunch on the hospital grounds. At this church service there was a special dedication of several plaques which listed the names of all the training school graduates, in memory of Dr. M.A.R. Young.

The church bulletin for the day records the event in these words: "Today in our worship we are remembering a host of people who made significant and lasting contributions to the life of the Archer Memorial Hospital, the community of Lamont, and this church... We are also remembering a beloved physician who gave freely the gifts of his heart and the skill of his hands and who was an important influence in the training and lives of many of these nurses. These plaques contain the names of the 595 graduates of the Lamont School of Nursing. We remember them and give thanks for them; and we dedicate this tribute to them in loving memory of Dr. Morley A.R. Young."

In 1992, an 80th Anniversary newsletter was produced, to "provide our community with more insight into the recent happenings in our community hospital." An overview of medical, nursing, diagnostic, special services, such as administration, dietary, pharmacy, plant maintenance, along with rehabilitation services, pastoral care, volunteer and community services gave an opportunity for the community to get to know the hospital better through words and photographs.

One of the notable things about the newsletter was its focus on the people who worked at the hospital. Dr. Peter Newbery, Director, United Church Health Services, commented in the newsletter that "An 80 year anniversary is one to be very proud of. When it can be celebrated with knowledge of the dedicated service, and high quality of work which so many have contributed... we can be proud indeed. And we give thanks for the many who have contributed so much."

ALL PHOTOS: LHCC

Photos from top to bottom:
Administrative staff:
Dolores Sadoway (right),
Anita Anderson (left)
Dietary: Jo-Anne Guglich
Housekeeping and Laundry:
Don Harsulla
Plant Maintenance:
Stu McNair
Nurse Manager:
Sheila Vilcsak, Long-Term Care

The church's involvement with the hospital at Lamont found a new focus during these times, as health reform began to come to the forefront. An ad hoc Support Group to the hospital was formed by the Alberta and Northwest Conference of the United Church of Canada in the early 1990's as a support for church involvement with the hospital. The support group was comprised of three people from the hospital and four from the United Church. The group saw that "As the face of health care changes, and as major and far-reaching decisions are being made about the values that will shape its future, the church's experience, involvement and voice are needed." The support group, in conjunction with the Health Care Task Group of the Alberta and Northwest Conference, worked to express the church's position on health care issues to various government bodies.

A presentation by the Support Group to the Division of Mission in Canada, United Church of Canada, on November 22, 1993, reviewed the commitment of the hospital to its mission and renewed the Church's commitment to support that mission. The Church itself was undergoing a change in the definition of its mission work: "Traditionally, our church has followed a community development model in health care. Hospitals were provided in remote areas and needy communities and then the church withdrew involvement when the community was able to continue the work... The United Church of Canada is in the process of revising its mission statement about health services. Like the United Church of Canada, Lamont Health Care Centre is finding its place in the new frontier." With a shift in the concept of "frontier", the new mission would come to recognize that new frontiers are always presenting themselves.

Lamont found, too, that it was not alone in offering a Christian perspective in health care. An organization of voluntary Christian health care providers in the province of Alberta was formed, to which the Lamont Health Care Centre belonged. A stronger voice for Christian health care was made possible through a collective voice.

Innovations in the provision of medical services to the community were introduced in the mid 1990's. Dr. Murray Schneider opened a chiropractic office, possibly the first to be included in a hospital setting in Alberta. A Palliative Care Program was established. A Women's Issues Committee looked at concerns of women in the medical context. Dr. Ray expanded his surgery training to include other laparoscopic procedures. A program called "Prevention for Life" was established, providing incentives for people to incorporate wellness practices into their lives. Another outgrowth of the program was the inclusion of health and wellness hints in the hospital's regular newsletter to the community.

BRIAN GAVRILOFF, THE EDMONTON JOURNAL used by permission

Fire lit up the sky over Lamont's hospital, May 30, 1995

KIRK HARROLD

Salvaging equipment and files from the medical clinic that was destroyed by the fire. The clinic was relocated to the basement of the County Office for seven months

Whereas 'fiscal restraint' had been a keyword in the past, 'restructuring' became the new word to describe the movement in health care in the province of Alberta in 1993-1994. Major events were occurring. Regionalization undertaken by the government eliminated all district hospital boards, and districts were restructured into 17 hospital regions. Boundaries to the regions had to be negotiated, then Regional Boards appointed by the Minister of Health, and three year business plans developed. All health facilities in a region would be part of the regional structure, including those run by the voluntary sector (all church-affiliated health care facilities such as Lamont Health Care Centre). The Honorable Shirley McClellan, Minister of Health, said that "...such facilities would operate under agreements with, and receive their funding from, the regional board." These voluntary facilities would retain their boards of management. Development of a Voluntary Agreement with the Minister of Health took time but in January, 1995, the Minister of Health signed the "Umbrella Agreement" ensuring the continuation of the voluntary sector.

The Lakeland Regional Health Authority was formed, of which Lamont became a part. One of the Regional Board's first responsibilities was to determine what facilities would offer services in the region and which ones would be eliminated. Active lobbying, vocal public forums, and input from all communities in the region preceded the final document from the Lakeland Regional Health Authority on Health Delivery in the Lakeland Health Region. The document stated about the future for Lamont: "Lamont will provide medical in-patient services (10 beds) and a continuation of surgical and 12 hour Emergency department services." Lamont would also retain its long-term care component. Cooperation and Service Agreements outlining the responsibilities of each party were signed between the Regional Health Authority and the Lamont Health Care Centre.

Issues of equity for voluntary facilities were challenging to resolve with the government as well. The Catholic Health Association of Alberta and Affiliates which now involved all of the faith-based facilities in Alberta was ultimately empowered to act as "one voice" to present the concerns of all voluntary facilities to the government. Paramount in their concerns were negotiating a new Owner's Equity agreement with the government, which would affect hospitals such as Lamont that were owned and operated by the voluntary sector.

On May 30, 1995, a fire destroyed a portion of the old hospital. Acute care, emergency services and the medical clinic were shut down by the fire. Nine patients in the acute care section in the 1948 wing were transferred to surrounding hospitals, while another 22 long-term patients were moved temporarily to the town's recreation centre. Eighty-one residents of the Auxiliary wing were unaffected, although there was a small amount of smoke and water damage to that area of the hospital. Thanks to the quick response of fire fighting crews from the regional disaster response team, and community volunteers who helped with the evacuation of patients, there were no injuries reported.

Elsie Warawa was recovering from surgery on the third floor of the 1948 wing when the fire started. "The alarm goes off. I'm in bed thinking there's nothing I can do. I can't get out of bed... Out of 365 days, I had to pick that one for surgery... We could have been burnt. We could have been barbequed... I just sensed that they (the nurses and volunteers) were going to come and get me... They worked like beavers, let me tell you."

The Board was committed to the restoration of services at the Lamont Health Care Centre as quickly as possible after the fire. The 1928 and 1948 wings of the hospital received the greatest damage and were ultimately demolished while the 1965 wing was renovated to restore emergency services and acute care beds. Willingdon Hospital, which had been closed by regionalization, was leased from the Sister Servants of Mary Immaculate to accommodate the long-term care residents displaced by the fire.

LHCC

Dr. Jaime Namit, 1995

A community service of thanksgiving and gratitude was held on July 2, 1995, recognizing the contributions of all those involved in the evacuation and fire fighting in assuring the safety of patients and residents. After some delays, the 1965 wing renovations were completed by January 16, 1996, and a special "Missioning Service" was held later on June 28, 1996, to recognize the restoration of medical care at the Archer Wing of the Lamont Health Care Centre.

The fire had forced the temporary relocation of the Lamont Clinic to the basement of the County Office, just a few blocks from the hospital, for a period of seven months. During this time, new faces appeared on the medical staff. In November, 1995, Dr. Jaime Namit arrived from New Brunswick, to begin his practice. Dr. Suresh Kanani became a member of the medical team April 1, 1996, and Dr. Karin Osiowy was granted associate medical staff membership at the Lamont Health Care Centre in October, 1996.

PEARL LETWIN

On March 31, 1996, Dr. John Sunley retired, after 35 years of dedicated service to the community and hospital

Earlier in March, 1996, Dr. John Sunley retired after 35 years at Lamont. A photograph of Dr. Sunley was placed in the front entrance with those of Dr. Young and Dr. Archer, in recognition of his contribution as Medical Superintendent, 1979-1988. According to an Alumnae newsletter note, Dr. Sunley was not retiring from medical practice completely, as he was planning on joining the Links Clinic in Edmonton in a part-time position.

Other changes that occurred during this time included the arrival of Margaret McCoy as supervisor of Physiotherapy. Nursing staff also underwent revisions due to budgetary restrictions, with adjustments in both hours and positions. A building project completed during this time was an upgrade to the Nursing Home and the Beaverhill Lodge that was undertaken in 1995-1996, with completion in early 1996.

LHCC

Dr. Suresh Kanani, 1996

There was a long space of time between the fire and the decision about Lamont hospital's future. In light of the issues of restructuring and downsizing, the future of the hospital had become a question. Insurance investigations and assessments were slow in coming, which only served to fuel the fears of many people that this would be the end of the hospital. Both staff and community also expressed their concerns for the future with significant budget cuts continuing within the new Region. The Director of Nursing Services, Evelyn Lopetinsky, recognized the effects on the staff when she wrote in a report to the Board, "The past few months have proven to be a period of much anxiety amongst the staff of our facility. Most feel that living with the unknown has been the most difficult."

PEARL LETWIN

During his visit in January, 1996,
Ralph Klein, Premier of Alberta, hears about
healthcare issues from Neville Calvert, long-time
resident at the Auxiliary Hospital

Despite of the delays and uncertainty, the Lamont Health Care Centre Board and administration continued the dialogue with the Alberta government and the Lakeland Region to plan the new facility. The local MLA, Ed Stelmach, lent his support to the effort. Input from the community was sought by way of a "Community Needs Assessment" conducted in November, 1995. This provided additional information regarding what the community perceived were important medical and health care concerns. Comments from the community included: "Loss of services and/or threatened loss of services is of great concern to our community and local trading area. It is imperative that we maintain at least all services available at the time of the fire"; "Will we be able to attract and keep physicians?"; "As senior citizens we do have travel concerns... We would much prefer to have as many aspects of medical treatment available here as possible."

A visit to the hospital by Premier Ralph Klein in January, 1996, was timely as those in attendance took the opportunity to raise their concerns about regionalization, health care cuts and future plans for the Lamont Health Care Centre.

DORIS ANDRAIS

Sod turning, Assisted Living, 1997
Left to right: Fred Pewarchuk,
Rev. Dave Edwards, Peter Zagrosh,
Kent Harrold

By March, 1996, the Master Plan for the Lamont Health Care Centre was completed, with the assistance of Resource Management Consultants (RMC). After amendments, it was submitted to the government. Approval for the plan was received in July, 1996, and an announcement was made that, along with the $4.5 million in payouts from insurance, $5.3 million in provincial money would be made available for rebuilding the Lamont Health Care Centre. The firm of Alastair Cockburn, Architect, was retained for the project, and plans were initiated.

Phase one of the project was the renovations to the old Archer Memorial Hospital, following the fire. Once that project was completed, at a cost of $1.2 million, the Active Care beds were fully utilized, and all support services were operational. Day surgery had increased, as had the use of emergency services.

Phase two of the capital project was the construction of a Senior Citizens' Assisted Living Complex. This concept had its birth in discussions of the Board in 1994, when it was determined that another level of care could be provided to seniors who wished to live independently. The plan included 20 apartment rental suites, all of which were to be fully wheelchair accessible. Meals and laundry services could be purchased, while housekeeping and an emergency call service would be part of the rental package. Access to the hospital amenities and physician's offices would be made through a link to the proposed new Health Care Centre. The $1.4 million for this project came from the Board of Management.

The approval to go ahead with phase three of the capital project was received in March, 1998. The construction of the new acute care and frail elderly units would cost $11.9 million, of which $6.911 was contributed by the province of Alberta. The new facility would house 14 Acute Care beds, 20 Continuing Term Care beds (in addition to the 81 beds in the Auxiliary and Nursing Home wings), 2 Respite Care beds, 2 Palliative Care beds, 6 Day Surgery beds, 4 emergency beds (2 trauma, 2 observation) and 2 Operating Rooms (1 major and 1 minor), X-ray, laboratory, rehabilitation therapies, and all necessary support services. Community programs such as Home Care, Public Health, and the Medical Clinics of Drs. Ray & Kanani and Dr. Namit would be housed in the old Archer Memorial Hospital.

KIRK HARROLD

The Assisted Living Complex was officially opened on April 16, 1998, to provide independent yet supported living accommodation for seniors

On April 16, 1998, the Assisted Living Complex was officially opened. The general contractor, Synergy Projects Ltd. had completed the building in just seven months. Representatives of the Alberta Government, the United Church, and the Board of Management of the Lamont Health Care Centre joined about 150 people in the common room of the new complex. Following the ribbon-cutting ceremony for the Assisted Living Complex, visitors were encouraged to tour the facility to view the many accommodations that had been built into the facility to meet the needs of seniors.

DORIS ANDRAIS

Lamont Health Care Centre sod turning ceremony, April 16, 1998
Left to right:
Dr. Peter Newbery,
Kent Harrold,
Stan Woloshyn,
Dareld Cholak,
Ed Stelmach

KIRK HARROLD

Lamont Lions Club donates a cheque towards landscaping the new facility

A sod-turning ceremony to officially signal the beginning of the building project was held later that same afternoon. Greetings and congratulatory remarks were brought by Fred Pewarchuk, Mayor of Lamont; Dr. Peter Newbery, United Church of Canada; Reeve Mae Adamyk, County of Lamont #30; Dareld Cholak, Board Chairman, Lakeland Regional Health Authority; The Honorable Stan Woloshyn, Minister, Alberta Public Works and Services, among others.

The community, always supportive of its hospital, turned out to help celebrate. Their support was felt in other ways as well. The Board of Management had put in place a building fund to accept donations for supplementary equipment and services, and to furnish rooms in the new facility. The community responded warmly and generously to the plan, with donations from organizations and memorials to individuals enabling such "extras" as the helipad, landscaping and Assisted Living patios. Contributions to furnishing the rooms in the Acute Care wing were made by numerous community and church groups, families, and individuals. Their contributions have been acknowledged by brass plaques outside each of the Acute Care rooms. The community's response prompted Kent Harrold to say, "The magnitude of support from our community has been extremely gratifying and underlies people's sense of ownership in their hospital."

Lamont Health Care Centre was able to provide services to other health care facilities in the Region. These services included Fiscal Management services to the Lodge Foundation, as well as laundry services to hospitals in Radway, Fort Saskatchewan, and Redwater, Beaverhill Lodge and the Town of Lamont. Harold James also became Area 1 Manager for the Region, under a special arrangement for his services.

KIRK HARROLD

The new Lamont Health Care Centre under construction

KIRK HARROLD

The central nursing station in the new facility (fondly known as the "centre of the universe") before the move of staff and patients

The construction of the new facility was now the responsibility of Aman Building Corporation, who had been successful in their tender that was submitted in February, 1998. Construction was completed on schedule and on budget. The various departments and services were able to move into the new building in late April, 1999. In early May, the long-term care residents who had been housed at Willingdon since the fire of 1995 were moved to the new rooms in Continuing Care, and patients from the Acute Care in the old Archer building were transferred to the new facility.

Renovations then began on the Archer building to accommodate the Public Health, Home Care and Children's Services offices on the second floor. The top floor renovations included three suites to accommodate visiting nursing and medical personnel on a short-term basis. The lower floor was renovated to enlarge office space for the physicians and visiting specialists in podiatry, chiropractic, and gerontology.

Catching up on people:

- *Florence Love, Class of '22, Alumnae Association advocate, and author of "The Lamp is Golden" passed away in December, 1989*
- *L. Marie Young passed away December 26, 1992 at the Lamont Auxiliary Hospital*
- *L. "Bud" Haverstock retired from the Pharmacy Department, September, 1995*

To preserve the memory of those who had contributed to the hospital over the years, the Acute Care wing of the hospital was named after Dr. A.E. Archer. The Assisted Living Complex was named Morley Young Manor, after Dr. M.A.R. Young.

Integrating the past, present and future was a goal of those who created the new Lamont Health Care Centre. Integrating faith-based health care with a secular society, and fiscal responsibility with a caring for people proved to be a challenge.

However, at Lamont, there is a heritage of such accomplishments. Kent Harrold, Board Chairman, wrote in an article for *Health and Healing*, Winter, 1999: "A sense of Christian mission embracing service, stewardship, innovation, and connectedness with community have been the hallmarks of health care delivery in Lamont for almost a century. It is intended that tradition will continue."

LAMONT HEALTH CARE CENTRE

OFFICAL OPENING – SEPTEMBER 9, 1999

TRUDY HARROLD

Lamont Health Care Centre, Board of Management

Back row, left to right: Pat Hryniw, Mae Adamyk, Rev. Dave Edwards, Doris Andrais, Janet Jenkins

Front row, left to right: Peter Zagrosh, Kent Harrold

Below: The Lamont Health Care Centre

TRUDY HARROLD

KIRK HARROLD

Above: Ed Stelmach, MLA and Minister of Infrastructure (right) and Halvar Jonson, Minister of Health and Wellness (2nd from right) join Board member Mae Adamyk and Executive Director Harold James in an informal chat at the opening ceremonies

KIRK HARROLD

Dr. Mihir Ray, Chief of Medical Staff at the Lamont Health Care Centre, was one of the speakers

DORIS ANDRAIS

DORIS ANDRAIS

Top: Cutting one of the five ribbons to officially open the Lamont Health Care Centre is Board Chairman, Kent Harrold, assisted by Rev. Dave Edwards

Above: Doris Andrais, Mistress of Ceremonies for the Official Opening, introduced speakers and presenters to the crowd

KIRK HARROLD

Left: Over 350 people from the community attended the ceremonies and enjoyed refreshments prepared by the Dietary Staff of LHCC

LAMONT HEALTH CARE CENTRE MISSION STATEMENT

We believe that wholeness of body, mind and spirit
is God's will for every person.

We commit ourselves to the promotion of health,
the healing of illness,
the care of the elderly and the disabled
and the well-being of the community.

LHCC

A new pin was designed to celebrate the Lamont Health Care Centre. Incorporating the symbols of the United Church of Canada, the Town of Lamont, and the County of Lamont, it captured both the spirit of cooperation among the participants, and the sense of mission behind the Centre.

The following people were involved in the Lamont Health Care Centre, as of September 1, 1999

BOARD OF MANAGEMENT:
Chairman: Kent Harrold
Vice Chairman: Peter Zagrosh
Rev. Dave Edwards
Pat Hryniw
Doris Andrais
Janet Jenken
Mae Adamyk

ADMINISTRATION:
Executive Director: Harold James
Executive Secretary: Dolores Sadoway
Director of Finance: Jim Burger
Payroll Clerk: Judy Robinson
Purchasing Officer: Shirley Konsorada
Office Staff: Anita Anderson, Lorraine Field, Kim Yarusiewich, Shirley Ropchan, Kim Palmer

MEDICAL STAFF – ACTIVE:
Dr. Mihir Ray
Dr. Karin Kilpatrick
Dr. Jaime Namit
Dr. Elsbeth Van Arkel
Dr. Suresh Kanani

MEDICAL STAFF – ACTIVE CONSULTANTS:
Dr. R. Harris, Ophthalmology
Dr. B. Turner, Psychogeriatric Medicine
Dr. J. Heston, Ophthalmology
Dr. W.S. Hnydyk, Palliative Care
Dr. M. Kutzner, Ophthalmology
Dr. E. Weins, Surgery
Dr. D. Skelton, Geriatric Medicine
Dr. P.M. Johnson, Internal Medicine

MEDICAL STAFF – COURTESY:
Dr. B. Bose
Dr. G. Jones
Dr. G.S. Sidhu
Dr. S. DeWitt
Dr. G. Lippolt
Dr. J. Sunley
Dr. O. Farooq
Dr. L. Mittelsteadt
Dr. D.J. Toliver
Dr. M.Z. Hoque
Dr. L. Pfeiffer
Dr. L. Torok-Both
Dr. K. Hult
Dr. M.S. Sabir

DENTAL: Dr. W. Armstrong, Dr. D. Saleski
OPTOMETRY: Dr. P. Rogaski
PODIATRY: Dr. S.R. Hollingsworth, Dr. D.T. Gibbs

DEPARTMENT SUPERVISORS:
Radiology: Ann Kendall
Laundry/Housekeeping: Don Harsulla
Laboratory: David Stahl
Plant Maintenance: Stu McNair
Pharmacy: Diane Donnan
Dietary: Jo-Anne Guglich
Rehabilitation: Margaret McCoy
Medical Records: Gloriann Sarafinchin
Recreation: Wendy Horricks
Office/Purchasing: Jim Burger

PASTORAL CARE SERVICES: Rev. Dave Edwards

DIRECTOR OF NURSING SERVICES: Evelyn Lopetinsky

NURSE MANAGERS: Sheila Vilcsak, Long Term Care; Grace Stach, Acute/LTC; Pat Woodworth, Surgical

NURSING STAFF:
Natalie Adamyk, Jean Anderson, Kenny Balsillie, Wendy Baron, Janice Beck, Irene Begg, Marilyn Bell, Karin Berggren, Rhonda Bilocerkowec, Bernadette Boettger, Gerda Bonkowski, Tammy Borys, Vicky Bryks, Karen Carter, Karin Corrin, Michael Cote, Wanda Craigen, Barbara Danyluk, Amanda Deck, Denise Deck, Monica Dobroski, Diana Eastwood, Christine Engman, Cheryl Erickson, Pamela Evenson, Gloria Fedyniak, Joanne Frechette, Christine Glasier, Shirley Gluckie, Hazel Hackett, Pat Jabusch, Pat Jackson, Sharon Johnston, Holly Kelemen, Robin Klein, Joan Knauer, Florence Knezacek, Aline Therese Koroluk, Krista Koroluk, Allison Kostiuk, Elaine Kotyk, Tracy Kotyk, Deanna Kroeker, Joanne Kuchera, Crystal Lynn Kwashuk, Alyson Laird, Darlene Laughington, Sharon MacLean, Pauline Marler, Brenda Mayer, Mary McCartney, Maria McDonnell, Teresa Medynski, Donna Melnyk, Diane Miller, Jo Ann Namit-Gagnon, Frances Nelson, Nicole Onushko, Beverly Pawluk, Tammy Pawluk, Cindy Perillat, Mary Pierce, Deborah Plooy, Angie Procyk, Krysta Pryatel, Laura Pryatel, Debbie Pryatel, Kim Pshyk, Donna Pullishy, Karen Radke, Iris Radziwon-Kliachik, Annette Renyk, Ronald Renyk, Sharon Robertson, Emily Robinson, Shawn Sadoway, Phyliss Schamahorn, Carole Schinkinger, Patricia Schneider, Loraine Schreiber, Suzanne Schuit, Helen Schwanke, Jacqueline Senych, Sheila Sharun, Virginia Shewchuk, Tracy Shostak, Violet Shostak, Linda Seiker, Rose Skripitsky, Linda Smiley, Michelle Spilde, Charlene Stach, Jill Stadnick, Lindsay Stadnick, Margaret Storozhenko, Dixie Stumpf, Susan Swallow, Christina Taylor, Rose Vandelannoite, Erin Elizabeth Vander Hoek, Andrea Varga, Ann Warshawski, Denise Wasylucha, Lynda Jean Weleschuk, Evelyn Yost

SUPPORT STAFF:
Linda Baille, Janet Boelsgaard, Caroline Breitzke, Laureen Brown, Deborah Bryks, Ann Chernyk, Janet Effa, Pauline Eleniak, Linda Farris, Robin Field, Susan Fraser, Brandy Froescul, Charlotte Froescul, Diane Geislinger, Kathy Geislinger, Ryan Glasier, Adeline Gurba, Judy Harsulla, Sherry Ann Harvey, Brianna Herchek, Roseann Herchek, Joanne Hrynew, Jason James, Randy Jonker, Ann Jonker, Mieczyslaw Kabut, Jeanette Kadatz, Josie Kashuba, Victoria Latko, Sandra Lazarenko, Irene Letwin, Alayna Mackay, Sonia Mackay, Richard Mandryk, Jolene Medynski, Susan Milburn, Shirley Olynyk, Carmen Palahniuk, Carol Palichuk, Melissa Pryatel, Victoria Rajtmajer, Sumit Ray, Mike Robinson, Robert Sawchuk, Laurel Sharun, Bernadette Sheptyski, Steve Shostak, Shannon Skripitsky, Sharon Snyder, Jeanet Sobkow, Anna Steblyk, Lori Threinen, Tammy Trenholm, Chris Tychkowsky, Kimberly Wagil, Cherry Wilson

SOURCES

LOCAL HISTORY BOOKS:

Along Victoria Trail – Lamont and Area
From Bush to Bushels – Bruderheim and Area
Pride in Progress – Chipman, St. Michael, Edna/Star and Districts

LAMONT PUBLIC HOSPITAL/ ARCHER MEMORIAL HOSPITAL ARCHIVES:

Summaries of hospital history by Dr. Young, Dr. Sunley
"An Adventure in Friendship" – pamphlet, 1946
Western Hands are Sure – video released by the Committee on Missionary Education of the United Church of Canada, 1946
A Lamp is Golden – Lamont and its Nurses 1912-1962, Florence A. Love, Edmonton, Alberta, 1962
Photographs

DR. YOUNG ARCHIVES:

Photographs,writings, diplomas, awards

LPH/AMH ALUMNAE ARCHIVES:

Summaries of School of Nursing by L. Marie Young, Ethel James
Biographies of Nursing Students, compiled 1987
Photo albums, scrapbooks
Yearbooks:1926-1972
A.E. Archer Memorial Lectures

LAMONT AUXILIARY AND NURSING HOME ARCHIVES:

Photo albums, newspaper clippings
Special event records (photographs, newspaper clippings)

UNITED CHURCH ARCHIVES:

Anniversary booklets for Lamont
Other Lamont-related material from the Division of Mission in Canada

CITY OF EDMONTON ARCHIVES:

Newspaper clippings
Blueprints of building additions

PROVINCIAL ARCHIVES OF ALBERTA:

Photographs
Newspaper and other publication clippings

LAMONT HEALTH CARE CENTRE:

Minutes and Committee records
Special event records (photographs, newspaper clippings, speeches)